An Anthology of scripture Songs

by
Miriam Therese Winter

Medical Mission Sisters   Philadelphia, PA

Published by
Medical Mission Sisters
8400 Pine Road, Philadelphia, PA 19111

Printed by
Interstate Book Manufacturers, Inc.
Olathe, Kansas 66061

Layout and Design: Donald Carlton

This edition has been made possible through the generous assistance of
Vanguard Music Corporation of New York City and World Library Publications
of Cincinnati, Ohio. Miriam Therese Winter and the Medical Mission Sisters
are especially grateful to their publishers for permission to reprint songs
previously published under the following collection titles:

Avant Garde Records, Inc./Vanguard Music Corporation   (AG)
1595 Broadway, Room 313, New York, NY 10019
    JOY IS LIKE THE RAIN   (JOY)
    I KNOW THE SECRET   (SCT)
    KNOCK, KNOCK   (KK)
    SEASONS   (SEA)
    IN LOVE   (IL)
    GOLD, INCENSE AND MYRRH   (GIM)
    MASS OF A PILGRIM PEOPLE   (MPP)
    RSVP: LET US PRAY   (RSVP)
    SONGS OF PROMISE   (SP)
Record albums and various music editions (piano accompaniment,
full harmony, individual octavo arrangements for choirs) are available
from the publisher.

World Library Publications, Inc.   (WLP)
2145 Central Parkway, Cincinnati, Ohio 45214
    SANDSTONE   (SS)
    REMEMBER ME   (RM)
Record albums, cassettes, and a piano accompaniment/full harmony
music edition are available from the publisher.

In this edition, the publisher/publication source for each song is listed next to the individual
song title in the Index. Code letters identifying publishers and published collections are listed
above. The code PC/MMS refers to the Private Collection of the Medical Mission Sisters.

Scripture songs celebrate an experience of God. They are the people's song of praise for the One who intervenes on behalf of those unconditionally loved. Love songs, life songs - such in fact are the psalms, those lyrical expressions of trust, gratitude, anguish, full of all the pathos and enthusiasm of human experience in a given time and place. Many were personal reflections of those who walked with God. Some, corporately appropriate, were incorporated into public worship, and thereby survived. Separate collections kept by the community as the best of cultic expression have come down to us in a more ancient anthology which we call the Psalter, that once timely Songbook of the Second Temple. These psalms and other song fragments embedded in the Old Testament canon have been preserved for us as paradigms, examples of how life songs can indeed be scriptural.

With the new dispensation came a brand new song, Christological, christocentric, heralding an age in which eternal values were incarnate in human flesh. Deeply rooted in this world yet always reaching beyond it, the emerging scriptures of the early Church sing of the One who was handed over for our redemption, the One whom God vindicated by raising him up in glory. The whole of salvation history was redefined in relation to the One who had come to make all things new. New Testament hymns and credal fragments, indeed all the songs of the Bible, validate the appropriation of traditional themes and their contemporary re-expression.

It is biblical to sing of the *mirabilia Dei*, the wonderful works of God in the past, here and now, and to come. It is biblical to appropriate a scriptural word and rearticulate it in the present tense, trusting the Spirit to guarantee that essential meanings are transmitted intact. To be restricted solely to the received text is to risk missing its essential spirit, one that must be liberated again and again from the limitations of any one time or place. All human expression is historically and culturally conditioned. There is no universal song. There is simply universal Spirit, timeless, eternal, to be enfleshed in every age of history as testament to a living faith.

In the deepest sense of the word, the songs collected here are biblical, born of a dialogue with scripture and the realities of life. In season and out of season, the struggle to integrate behavior and belief has been the ultimate liturgy, where song has chronicled God's abiding presence through every season of the heart. These songs were sung in response to the Word's proclamation and they reflect the world I love, with all its pain and promise. The apple orchard in Philadelphia, the gates and the feel of Jerusalem, the sands of the Sinai desert, the grasslands and jungles of the African continent, the survival camps of the Cambodian refugees, the Alpine valleys of the Tyrol, Berlin with its devastating wall, London, Rome, Utrecht, Vancouver, Tasmania, the breakers of Fiji, the avenues of New York: there are traces of countless encounters in the spaces between the lines. Life is recorded here, to be remembered always. Such is the power of biblical song. In the word made melody, the past lives again in the present, through the song of those who seek to share an experience of God.

I give thanks and praise to the Lord who continually awakens my awareness, probing me, pushing me to question the quality of life. The more I sing of life, the more I learn of its mystery and meaning. Let us sing then of justice and liberation, of peace, compassion, and mercy, of healing and hope, love and longing, of wholeness and an end to all the hungers of the heart. Let us sing of a world where there is no more war, where none will ever be hungry or alienated or in want. Let us sing of that new and just society we labor to bring about. The God who cares intensely about this world is the God I seek and celebrate, the Lord who is the source of all scripture and the substance of my song.

Miriam Therese Winter
June 14, 1982

1/ Joy Is Like the Rain

Words and Music by
Sister Miriam Therese Winter

Moderately slow

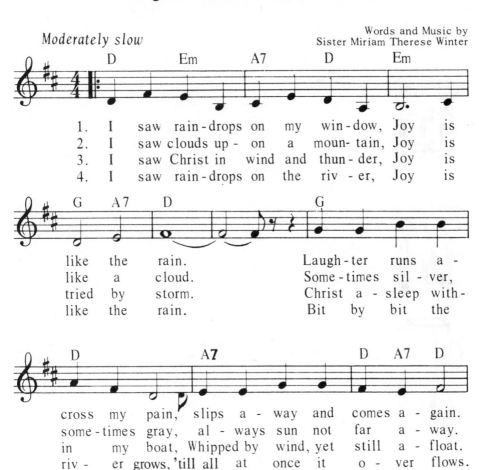

1. I saw rain-drops on my win-dow, Joy is
2. I saw clouds up-on a moun-tain, Joy is
3. I saw Christ in wind and thun-der, Joy is
4. I saw rain-drops on the riv-er, Joy is

like the rain. Laugh-ter runs a-
like a cloud. Some-times sil-ver,
tried by storm. Christ a-sleep with-
like the rain. Bit by bit the

cross my pain, slips a-way and comes a-gain.
some-times gray, al-ways sun not far a-way.
in my boat, Whipped by wind, yet still a-float.
riv-er grows, 'till all at once it o-ver flows.

Joy is like the rain.
Joy is like a cloud.
Joy is tried by storm.
Joy is like the rain.

Mt 8:23-27/Mk 4:35-41/Lk 8:22-25

2/ Zaccheus

Words and Music by
Sister Miriam Therese Winter

Calypso

There was a man in Jer - i - cho called Zac-

che-us. There was a man in

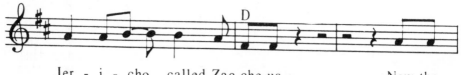

Jer - i - cho called Zac-che-us. Now the

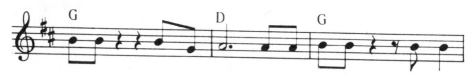

He-brews, they were tall, but Zac-che-us, he was

small, yet the Lord loved Zac-che-us, bet-ter than them all.

Lk 19:1-10

6

1. The Lord went walk-ing one day through
2. The Lord said: "Zac-che-us, I am din-ing with
3. Now Zac-che-us was small of sta-ture, but

Jer-i-cho town, and the peo-ple be-gan to
you to-day. Zac-che-us, I come to your
he could show, that a man who is stout of

gath-er from miles a-round. But Zac-che-us,
house, come lead the way." Then Zac-che-us,
heart can grow and grow. "If I have chea-ted

he could-n't see, so he climbed a syc-a-more
he gave a cheer, but the peo-ple be-gan to
young or old, I re-store the goods four-

tree, And the Lord looked up and said:
sneer. "This man is a sin-ner, does the Lord
fold." And sal-va-tion came that day to

"Zac-che-us, come down." There all.
seek lodg-ing here?"
his whole house-hold.

3/ Speak to Me, Wind

Words and Music by
Sister Miriam Therese Winter

Freely

1. Speak to me, wind, of my Lord. Talk to me, wind, of my
2. Speak to me, stars, of my Lord. Talk to me, stars, of my
3. Speak to me, trees, of my Lord. Talk to me, trees, of my
4. Speak to me, brook, of my Lord. Talk to me, brook, of my
5. Sing to me morn-ing and night. Shout it in dark-ness and

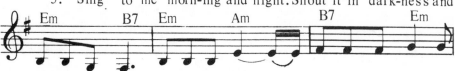

Sa-vior and Lord. I am a-lone, far from my home, a
Sa-vior and Lord. My lit-tle lamp leaps in the night. If
Sa-vior and Lord. My roots run deep to the land of my birth,
Sa-vior and Lord. I'm al-ways run-ning a-way from my source,
whis-per in light. My Lord is King, cre-a-tion is keen to

child in a storm who is rest-less-ly roam-ing. O
there be no oil, how shall it give light. O
yet ev'-ry branch lifts a-way from the earth. O
twist-ing and tumb-ling and los-ing my course. O
en-ter a King-dom that I've nev-er seen. O

1.2.3.4.

5. Em

speak to me, wind, of my Lord.
speak to me, stars, of my Lord.
speak to me, trees, of my Lord.
speak to me, brook, of my Lord.
sing to me morn-ing and night.

Gen 1:1-31

4/ Come Down, Lord

Words and Music by
Sister Miriam Therese Winter

Moderato

1. Come down, Lord, my son is ill, wracked with fe-ver
2. Come down, Lord, my soul is ill, wracked with an-guish
3. Come down, Lord, the world is ill, wracked with blood-shed

the live-long day. He is life to me, if you will,
the live-long day. All my sor-row-ing will be still,
the live-long day. We must strug-gle for peace un-til

drive death a- way, drive death a- way. Lord, do not
if You but say, if You but say. Lord, do not
You show the way, You show the way. Lord, do not

come to my house, I'm un-worth-y, speak and the
come to my house, I'm un-worth-y, speak and the
come to our house, we're un-worth-y, speak and the

prom-ise is sealed. For when Your Word, O God, is
prom-ise is sealed. For when Your Word, O God, is
prom-ise is sealed. For when Your Word, O God, is

spok-en, he shall be healed, he shall be healed.
spok-en, I shall be healed, I shall be healed.
spok-en, we shall be healed, we shall be healed.

Mt 8:5-13/Lk 7:1-10
Jn 4:46-54

5/ Spirit of God

Words and Music by
Sister Miriam Therese Winter

Moderately slow

1. Spir-it of God in the clear run-ning wa-ter,
2. I saw the scar of a year that lay dy-ing,
3. Spir-it of God, ev'-ry one's heart is lone-ly,

blow-ing to great-ness the trees on the hill.
heard the la-ment of a lone whip-poor-will.
watch-ing and wait-ing and hun-gry un-til,

Spir-it of God in the fin-ger of morn-ing,
Spir-it of God,   see that cloud cry-ing,
Spir-it of God, we   long that You on-ly full-

fill the earth, bring it to birth and blow

where you will.   Blow, blow, blow till I

be but breath of the Spir-it blow-ing in me.

Ps 104:30
Jn 3:8
Rm 8:19

6/ Howl, My Soul

Words and Music by
Sister Miriam Therese Winter

Moderato

1. Howl, you, for the day of the Lord is near.
2. Weep, you, for He comes to judge the land.
3. Sing, you, he was one of us. A-men!
4. Peace, you, there's no need to be a-fraid,

Howl, my soul, for the day of the Lord is here.
Weep, my soul, for none but the just shall stand.
Sing, my soul, for the Lord re-turns a-gain.
Peace, my soul, for he knows of what you're made.

Let ev-'ry knee be bent and ev-'ry head be bowed, for
He will come in a whirl-wind to up-root the trees, yet
He will breath new spi-rit in-to old dry bones,
Though moun-tains crum-ble when he bares his breast,

He will come like thun - der tear-ing up the cloud.
He will rock my soul as the gen-tle breeze.
trade a heart of flesh for a heart of stone.
in the crook of his arm I will lie to rest.

Howl, my soul, trem-ble, my soul, in fear.
Weep, my soul, for the judge-ment is at hand.
Sing, my soul, si-ng my soul, a-men.
Peace, my soul, it is the mo-ment for which you've prayed.

Made in the U.S.A.

I Kings 19:11-12
Is 13:6-13

Ezek 36:26;37:7-10
Joel 2:1-2
Lk 21:27

7/ It's a Long Road to Freedom

Words and Music by
Sister Miriam Therese Winter

It's a long road to free - dom,

a' wind-ing steep and high. But when you walk in

love with the wind on your wing and cov-er the

earth with the songs you sing, the miles fly by. ————

1. I walked one morn-ing by the sea,
2. I walked one morn-ing at the dawn,
3. I walked one morn-ing with a friend,
4. I walked one morn-ing with my King,

and all the waves reached out to me.   I
when bits of night still lin - gered on.   I
and prayed the day would nev - er end.   The
and all my win - ters turned to spring,   Yet

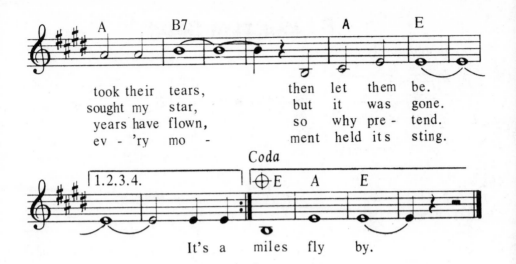

took their tears,   then let them be.
sought my star,   but it was gone.
years have flown,   so why pre - tend.
ev - 'ry mo -   ment held its sting.

It's a miles fly by.

Eph 5:2

8/ Pilgrim Song

Words and Music by
Sister Miriam Therese Winter

Moderately

1. We are lone - ly by birth. We are
(2) wind in the tree, we have
(3) grass on the lawn, we will
(4) long - ing for One, for a

on - ly like pil - grims on earth. Born to be
been rath-er reck-less and free. Thrown far and
pass by the way and be gone. A les - son to
song and a place in the sun, a home up a-

king, time is but a tem - po - ra - ry thing,
wide, we long to set - tle down be - side the
learn, we walk but once there's no re - turn.
bove where ev - 'ry day is lived in love, for

on - ly on loan while on earth. 2. Like the
stream flow - ing through e -ter - ni - ty. 3. Like the
Time____ is al-ways mov - ing on. 4. We are
rest when the jour - ney is done.

9/ How I Have Longed

Words and Music by
Sister Miriam Therese Winter

Moderato

1. How I have longed to draw you to My - self
2. walk-ing on the wings of the wind,
3. ho -ver at the tip of your heart,

as when a hen cov-ets her brood,
see My warm breast in the set-ting sun.
as a moth-er a-wait-ing a son;

but you went dart-ing like chicks in a storm,
Night is but sha-dow of my wings wide-spread, My
should a moth-er for-get the child of her womb, the

how could you know that My wing was warm, how could you
pin-ions pre-par-ing a bri-dal bed, when all your
joy when a loved one en-ters the room, I'll not for-

Chorus

know My love pur-sued.
toil and tears are done.
get My cho-sen one.

Come to me, my lit-

tle one, and you will be re-freshed and

I will give you rest. rest. 2. You'll hear me
3. Know that I

Ps 104:3   Mt 23:37/Lk 13:34
Is 49:15   Jn 14:3
Mt 11:28   Rev 21:1-4

10/ Ten Lepers

Words and Music by
Sister Miriam Therese Winter

Ten un-clean and no-where to go. Ten men cleansed as clean as snow. One re-turned to give God thanks, but nine went a-way.

1. Ten men, lep-ers in a Heb-rew town. Ten cry-ing: "Lord, won't You please come down." No hope near 'till one fine day, Je-sus of Na-za-reth passed that way.

2. "Lord make me clean" was their sin-gle cry. "See, how the whole world—pass-es us by. No one's home will take us in!" Then Christ bent down to touch their skin.

3. Like a tree—when its buds come true, or a patch of spring that is fresh and new, Christ re-stored the ones de-filed, gave them the flesh of a new-born child.

4. God gives gifts—to us ev-'ry day, fa-vors His peo-ple in ev-'ry way; Hope re-stored and pain re-lieved—Do you ev-er give thanks for a gift re-ceived?

5. Thank you, Lord—for the sum-mer sun, for sight and song and—good deeds done, for faith and fa-mi-ly and lov-ing friends, for the day that be-gins and the night that ends.

Lk 17:11-19

11/ God Gives His People Strength

Words and Music by
Sister Miriam Therese Winter

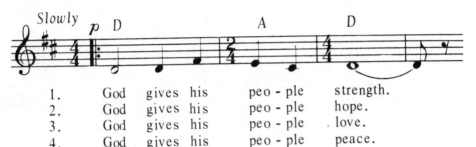

1. God gives his peo-ple strength.
2. God gives his peo-ple hope.
3. God gives his peo-ple . love.
4. God gives his peo-ple peace.

If we be-lieve in His way, He's swift to re - pay
If we but trust in His word, our prayers are al-ways heard.
If we but o-pen wide our heart, He's sure to do His part;
When sor-row fills us to the brim, and cour - age grows dim,

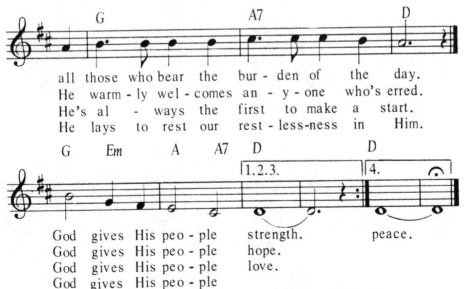

all those who bear the bur - den of the day.
He warm - ly wel - comes an - y - one who's erred.
He's al - ways the first to make a start.
He lays to rest our rest - less-ness in Him.

God gives His peo - ple strength. peace.
God gives His peo - ple hope.
God gives His peo - ple love.
God gives His peo - ple

Ps 29:11
Mt 11:28
1 Jn 4:19

12/ The Wedding Banquet

Words and Music by
Sister Miriam Therese Winter

I can-not come. I can-not come to the ban-quet, don't

trou-ble me now. I have married a wife. I have bought me a

cow. I have fields and com-mit-ments that cost a pret-ty

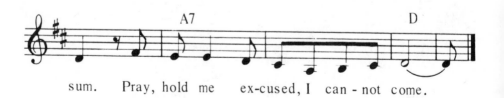

sum. Pray, hold me ex-cused, I can-not come.

Mt 22:1-14/Lk 14:15-24

1. A cer-tain man held a feast on his
2. The mas-ter rose up in an-ger, called his
3. When all the poor had as-sem-bled there was
4. Now God has writ-ten a les-son for the

fine es-tate in town. He laid a fes-tive ta-ble
ser-vants by name, said: "Go in-to the town, fetch
still room to spare, so the mas-ter de mand-ed
rest of our kind; if we're slow in re-spond-ing He

and wore a wed-ding gown. He sent in-vi-
the blind and the lame, fetch the peas-ant and the
"Go search ev'-ry-where - to the high-ways and the
may leave us be-hind. He's pre-par - ing a

ta-tions to his neigh-bors far and wide, but
pau - per for this I have willed: my
by - ways and force them to come in. My
ban-quet for that great and glo-rious day. When the

when the meal was rea-dy, each of them re-plied:
ban-quet must be crowd-ed, and my ta-ble must be filled."
ta-ble must be filled be-fore the ban-quet can be-gin."
Lord and mas-ter calls us, be cer-tain not to say:

13/ I Know the Secret

With feeling

Words and Music by
Sister Miriam Therese Winter

1. I know the se - cret of the wind   that turns my
2. I know the se - cret of the hearth   that burns the

win - ter a - wry.   I know   the se - cret of the
whole win - ter long.   It feeds   the fire   in my

storm that makes the child in me cry. Wild, but not
heart and it en - kin - dles my song. Faith, so like

e - ver as bad as it seems. There's warmth in the
tim - ber, is gif - ted with light.   Pro - mise of

whirl - wind   that shat-ters my dreams. It sel - dom
spring   in   a   long win - ter night. It's bright-ness

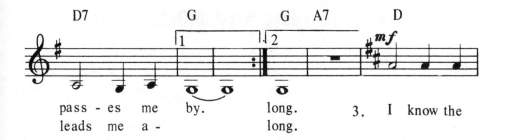

pass - es   me   by.   long.
leads   me   a -   long.   3. I know the

se - cret of the night   com-ing down like a bride.

One day its dress will be white and ev-'ry tear will be

dried. Sor - row and heart-ache will lin-ger no more. We'll know that

new-ness that we've wait-ed for, when all our win-ters have died.

I Kings 19:11-12
Rev 21:1-4

14/ He Bought the Whole Field

Words and Music by
Sister Miriam Therese Winter

Cheerfully

He bought the whole field for joy, he bought the

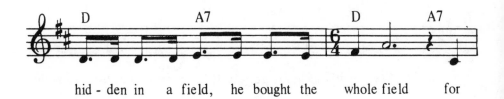

whole field for sheer joy. A man found a treas-ure, it was

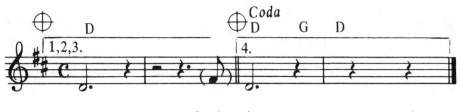

hid - den in a field, he bought the whole field for

joy. 2. A joy.
4. The

Mt 13:44
Mk 10:17-23
Lk 12:33-34
Acts 9:1-9,17-22
Phil 3:7-8

1. Paul was a He - brew by birth.
2. rich young man search- ing for truth,
3. Don't keep your treas - ure in a room
4. King - dom of heav-en we've found

He left his land to in - her - it the earth. He
who kept the com-mand - ments the whole of his youth, was
for a thief to steal, or a moth con-sume.
is so like a treas-ure hid - den in the ground. The

sowed God's Word and when the seed gave yield in the hearts
pro - mised a King-dom if he gave a-way all but he did-n't
All our gain, we count but loss, we are rich
ground is the peo- ple who long to be healed. If you real-ly

of a few, he bought the whole field. He bought the
have the vi - sion of Paul, who bought the
in Christ who chose a cross. He bought the
want the treas - ure, love the whole field. He bought the

15/ Yet I Believe

Words and Music by
Sister Miriam Therese Winter

Moderately

I be - lieve God lay sleep-ing in the tomb,

wait-ing un - til the day should break.   I be - lieve

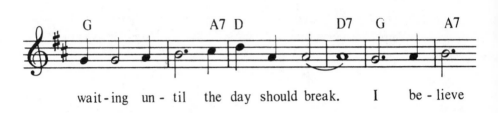

my Fa - ther has care of me and some-day,

He'll say, "My child, a - wake."   wake."

Jn 14:2; 19:41-42
Rm 8:36
I Co 15:30-31

D | A7 | D | A7

1. I be-lieve we were born to die   o - ver and
2. I be-lieve that the stars are mine. Love lifts the
3. I be-lieve I must go a - lone, tossed like a
4. I be-lieve we were born for joy. Some though, must

D | D7 | G | A7

o - ver a - gain.   I be - lieve that
stars from the night.   I be - lieve there's
wave on the sea.   Yet I be - lieve that
find it in pain.   Some riv - ers run through

D | [1 A7 G A7 D

we were meant to cry "A-men, my Lord, A - men."
al - ways sun to
we must have a
caves be - neath the

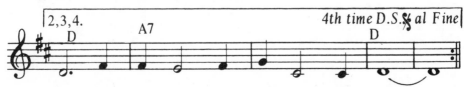

[2,3,4.   4th time D.S. al Fine|
D A7   D

2. shine, though some-times it's hid - den from sight.
3. home.   God holds a man - sion for me.
4. ground. Some-times there's sun ·in the rain.

16/ Come, Lord Jesus

Words and Music by
Sister Miriam Therese Winter

Gently

Verse D   G

1. Christ, come quick-ly, there's dan-ger at the
2. Want de-mands a hear-ing in far too man-y
3. world a-waits in dark-ness a might-y burst of
4. clouds shall send a Sav-ior like soft-ly fall-ing

D   E7

door, pov-er-ty a-plen-ty, hearts gone wild with
lands. The sick go un-at-tend-ed, death deals a heav-y
light, to set the lame one leap-ing, to give the blind one
rain, yet might-y in his pow-er, to free us from our

A   D   G

war. There's hun-ger in the cit-y and fam-ine on the
hand. Their dreams are often emp-ty, their cup of sor-row
sight. We have the proph-et's prom-ise, we a-wait the Prince of
chains. His shield will be com-pas-sion, his weap-on lib-er-

D mf Chorus   G   D G D

plain. Come, Lord Je-sus, the light is dy-ing, the night keeps
full.
Peace.
ty.

Em ⟶ p D   G   1,2,3.   4.
                                              D   D

cry-ing: Come, Lord Je - sus.(3 & 4. The)sus.

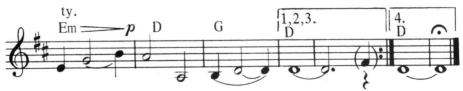

Is 9: 2; 35:4-6; 45:8; 61: 1-2
Rev 22: 20

17/ Easter Song

Words and Music by
Sister Miriam Therese Winter

Brightly

1. My Lord, he died for a King-dom to re-deem us
2. My Lord came forth like the morn-ing with the splen-dor
3. My Lord u - nit - ed our moun-tains with the ev - er -
4. My Lord re - newed all cre - a - tion that had wait-ed

from our sin. Now my peo-ple, don't you weep. He has
of the sun, came tri - umph-ant from the womb, from the
last-ing hills. Now the sea-sons and the sea sing his
late and long. Now we all with one ac - cord live and

ris - en from His sleep. He lives a - gain, this is our
dark-ness of the tomb, the vic - t'ry won,
song of vic - to - ry, rocks and rills,
love the Ris - en Lord. This is our song:

song, al - le - lu - ia. *Chorus*
al - le - lu - ia. Sing al - le - lu - ia, the Lord is

[1,2,3.] [4.]

ris - en, He is ris - en in -deed, al - le - lu - ia! ia!

Vanguard Music Corp., owner of publication and allied rights throughout the world.
International Copyright Secured   Made in the U.S.A.

Dt 33:13-15
Lk 24:34
Jn 20:11

Rm 8:19-23
I Co 15:54-57

18/ Don't Worry

Words and Music by
Sister Miriam Therese Winter

Don't wor- ry a-bout food or what you are to

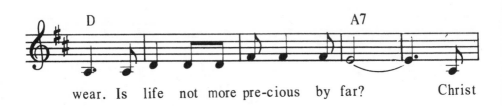

wear. Is life not more pre-cious by far? Christ

clothes you in His im- age and feeds you with His

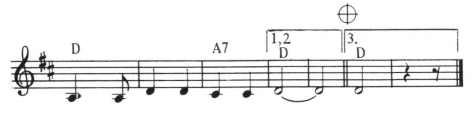

flesh and loves you as you are. are.

Mt 6:25-34/Lk 12:22-31
Jn 4:13-14; 6:35,53
Rm 8:29
Rev 3:18-21

1. Lord,   hear me,   this hun-ger   in   my heart
2. Lord,   I   drink   and still   I   thirst for   more;   I
3. Lord, I'm a   pau-per   be-fore   the throne of   God,

has been   a   crav-ing that's con-sumed me from the start.
hear Your liv - ing wa - ter   go   rush - ing   past   my door.
I   am in tat-ters,   my   feet are   un -shod.

Where shall I   find   bread   that   I   may eat my   fill
Give me   to   drink,   as - suage my burn-ing   thirst
I would have   vir - tue   to   hide my   nak-ed-ness.

and feed   my   weak-'ning   will.   Don't
and leave   my   soul   im - mersed.   Don't
Lord, who will   give   me   dress?   Don't

19/ Ballad of the Prodigal Son

Words and Music by
Sister Miriam Therese Winter

Rather slow

Verse

1. There was a man and he had two sons;
   boy went wild, his ways were free,
   boy cried out: "I'm feed-ing swine
   boy re - turned to his fa - ther's land.

the young-er one was but a boy when he
He squan-dered all his pro-per - ty. Then one
while my fath-er's house a - bounds with wine. I will
He longed to be but a hir-ed hand. Far a-

asked for his in-her-i - tance that he might en-
day there came a fa - mine, and he knew
go home to my fa - ther and I will
cross the va-cant val - ley the fa - ther

joy what life had to of - fer, and he left his home-land.
want and he knew hun - ger and he was lone-ly.
say I am un - wor-thy to be called a son."
saw his son re - turn-ing and he ran to meet him:

1,2,3. Chorus

The fa - ther wait - ed, al - le - lu - ia.

Lk 15:11-32

20/ God Loves a Cheerful Giver

Words and Music by
Sister Miriam Therese Winter

**Fast and joyous
(Whistle)**

God loves a

cheer-ful giv-er, give it all you've got. He loves to hear you

laugh-ing when you're in an awk-ward spot. When the odds add up a-

gainst you, it's time to stop and sing: "Praise God!" To praise him

is a joy-ous thing.   joy-ous thing.

Job 1:21; 42:10
Jon 1:1-3,17
Jn 18:15-17,25-27
2 Co 9:7

G   A

1. Pe - ter al - ways made a fuss, Pet-er was im-
2. Jon- ah was a gloom-y sort, he al-ways had a
3. Ho - ly Job was rich-ly blessed, he lost it all but

C   D7

pet - u - ous; he knew hard times when he de - nied his
sad re - port, he ran from God, he ran and he set
stood the test, for Job was stead -fast in his mis - er -

G

Lord. But hard - ly had he fal - len when he
sail. His jour - ney's end was quite ab - rupt, a
y. "God gives to me, He takes a - way, blessed

A   C   D7

got right up, be - gan a - gain. The con - stan -
fish came by and swallowed him up. He spent three
be the name of God this day." And he was

G

cy of Je - sus was his re - ward.
dark and drear - y days in - side the whale.
doub - ly blessed for his fi - del - i - ty.

21/ A Virgin

Words and Music by
Sister Miriam Therese Winter

Tenderly

1. Down past the Jor - dan, two thou-sand years a - go,   the
2. One   day an an - gel   sought the Vir-gin maid,
3. dark - ness of night then was driv - en   a - way   as

riv - ers of joy had long ceased to flow. Cre-a -tion was
said to her: "Ma-ry,   do not be a - fraid.   You have been
riv - ers of light poured from the womb of day.   New life was

tast-ing the Lord's a - veng-ing rod, sin had cast   us   from
des-tined to   bear God's   son," and the Vir - gin re-plied:
giv - en   to those   who be-lieved in the Prom-ised One

Gen 3:13-19
Lk 1:26-38
Rev 12:1-5

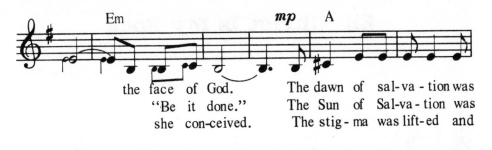

the face of God. The dawn of sal-va - tion was
"Be it done." The Sun of Sal-va - tion was
she con-ceived. The stig - ma was lift-ed and

mak - ing its start, for a Vir - gin bore Christ Je - - - -
pierc -ing the gloom, for a Vir - gin bore Christ Je - - - -
Sa - tan was hurled, for a

sus in her heart. 3.The Vir - gin bore Christ
sus in her womb.

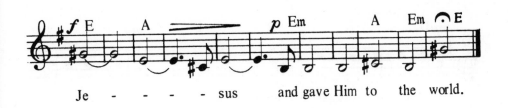

Je - - - - sus and gave Him to the world.

22/ Christ Is My Rock

Words and Music by
Sister Miriam Therese Winter

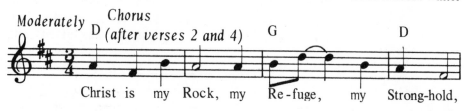

Christ is my Rock, my Re-fuge, my Strong-hold,

Firm as the tree's root that clut-ches the land. We who have faith

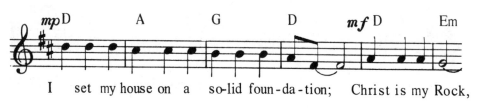

build with-out wor-ry, not like the man who builds up-on sand.

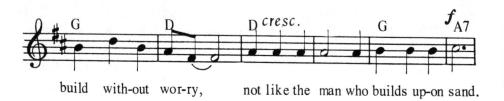

I set my house on a so-lid foun-da-tion; Christ is my Rock,

the root of my soul's re-cre-a - - tion. tion.

Ps 18:1-2
Mt 7:24-27

	D		G	D	

1. I know a man who loved to live free.
2. I know a man who loved to live high.
3. I know a man, a cool one to know.
4. I know a man who built out of straw. The

D   E7   A7

He pitched his tent by the side of the sea. It
He built his cas-tle near up to the sky. Through
He built his house out of ice and of snow. In
flim-si- est fel-low that I e -ver saw.

D   G

stood near the surf and was washed by the spray, Till
sum-mer and spring it stood pret-ty well, when
chill i - so - la - tion his night work was done, but it
One day a spark set it to flame, and

D   A   A7   D

one day a wave came and washed it a - way.
win - ter winds whis-tled it top - pled and fell. (Chorus)
melt- ed a - way with the warm morn-ing sun.
noth- ing was left to re - mem - ber his name. (Chorus)

23/ Peter

Words and Music by
Sister Miriam Therese Winter

Moderately

Chorus:

Come to me o-ver the wa-ter, Pe-ter; walk on the waves of the storm-ing sea. I know your boat is frail and fra-gile, but be-lieve in me. (2) My

1. I can do an-y-thing when faith does-n't weak-en.
2. peo-ple called out from the burn-ing des-ert.

See, the sea sleeps in the palm of my hand.
I turned a rock to a bub-bling spring.

My love's a light that leads like a bea-con to the
Those who be-lieve will nev-er be want-ing for

Prom - ised Land. lieve in me.
an - y-thing.

Ex 13:21-22; 17:6   Is 48:21   Mt 14:28-33   Jn 14:12-14

24/
Come to the Springs of Living Water

Words and Music by
Sister Miriam Therese Winter

Come to the springs of liv-ing wa-ter flow-ing

from the heart of God. God.

Verse

1. Come from the dis-tant val-ley to the moun-tain of the
2. Come with your pre-cious oint-ment to the moun-tain of the
3. Come with gui-tars and cym-bals to the moun-tain of the

Lord. Come from the far-off is-lands to God. Na-
Lord. Come with your hum-ble off'-rings to God. Come
Lord. Come with your mus-ic sing-ing to God. Lift

tions a-rise, Cast the cloud of dark-ness from your eyes.
to him now, has - ten to pay him your vows.
up your voice, ours is the God of Ja-cob, re-joice!

Vanguard Music Corp., owner of publication and allied rights throughout the world.
International Copyright Secured   Made in the U.S.A.

Ps 33:2-3   *For chords in parentheses, Capo 2   Is 2:2-3; 55:1; 60:1-4
Ps 76:11   Jn 7:37-38
Ps 150:3-5

25/ Knock, Knock

Words and Music by
Sister Miriam Therese Winter

Knock, Knock, the door will o - pen.
Seek and you will find. Ask, you will re -
ceive. God is ge - ne - rous and kind.

1. My friend, my cup - board's emp - ty.
2. Christ said to keep in - sist - ing.
3. Lord God, I come be - fore you.

Lend me loaves of bread. A guest has come a
Knock and do not cease. If they won't give out of
Giv - er of gifts, I plead. I'm poor and emp - ty

Lk 11:5-13

dis - tance, Need - ing to be fed. Go a-
friend - ship, they'll give to get some peace. You
hand - ed and nak - ed in my need. What

way, the door is shut now. Do
can't pre - dict the mo - ment.
fa - ther will take a scor - pion Or

not dis - turb my sleep. My
Read - y or not, it's here. At the
hand his child a stone? God's

chil - dren and I are comfort - a - ble, your
time you're least pre - pared for it, Christ's
sure to give the best of gifts to the

nag - ging need will keep. ——— Knock,
need - y will ap - pear. ——— Knock,
ones He calls His own. ——— Knock,

kind.

26/ Three Tents

Words and Music by
Sister Miriam Therese Winter

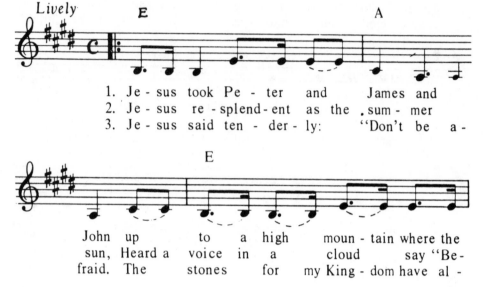

1. Je - sus took Pe - ter and James and
2. Je - sus re - splend - ent as the sum - mer
3. Je - sus said ten - der - ly: "Don't be a-

John up to a high moun - tain where the
sun, Heard a voice in a cloud say "Be-
fraid. The stones for my King - dom have al -

sun shone up - on Him. The glo - ry of
lov - ed one." At the sound of the
read - y been laid. Tell the vi - sion to

God was re - vealed in His face.
thun - der Pe - ter fell on his face cry - ing:
no - one till I go and re - turn, By this

Mt 17: 1-9/Mk 9: 2-9/Lk 9: 28-36

27/ Christ Is King

Words and Music by
Sister Miriam Therese Winter

Christ is King of heav-en and earth,—— Lord of life and death and birth,———— The whole world's wis-dom and it's worth.———— The

Last time F(E) *Verses*

1.
2. A
3. From
4.

Sing, you sea - sons, Win - ter and Spring.
light shall shine and sha - dow will cease,
sea to sea His love will live and grow.
Hail, Christ Je - sus, Lamb who was slain,

Ps 72:8, 12-14
Is 9:2-7
Rev 5:11-13

*For chords in parentheses, Capo 1

44

Sing, you crea - tures, to
And with His com - ing our
He will lift all those who have
Who gave up a king - dom and re -

C7 (B7)   **F (E)**

hon - or our King. —— Sing, ———— sing, ——
joy will in - crease.—— He shall be called ——
fall - en low, —— And ev - 'ry deed of
stored it a - gain. —— We thank You for your

Bb (A)   **F (E)**

ev - er - y —— liv - ing thing.————
won - der - ful, The Prince of Peace.————
dark - ness He will o - ver - throw. ————
glo - ri - ous and gen - tle reign. ————

F (E)

worth. ————————————————

28/ Father, Thy Will Be Done

Words and Music by
Sister Miriam Therese Winter

Moderately, with feeling

Chorus

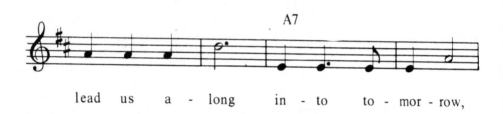

Is there a song to ease our sor - row, To

lead us a - long in - to to - mor - row,

To show us how to live in our now? Fa - ther, Thy

will be done. Fa - ther, Thy will be done.

Mt 6:10
Mt 26:39/Lk 22:42

Verses

1. What have you done for my friends?—— How have you
2. What have you done for my Son? —— Have you been

loved? —— How have you lived? How have you died?
kind? —— Have you re - ceived? Have you been wide?

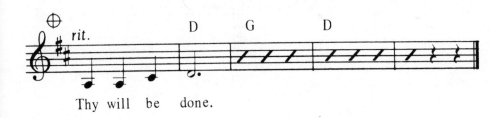

How did you give? How have you tried? ——————
Have you be - lieved? Have you been tried? ——————

Thy will be done.

29/ Changin'

Words and Music by
Sister Miriam Therese Winter

Bright

Chorus D   G

Chang - in', ——— times are   chang - in'.

D   A7

Some peo - ple think it's a **shock-ing** shame that

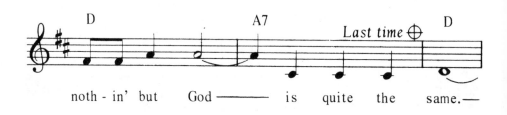

D   A7   *Last time* ⊕   D

noth - in' but God ——— is quite the same.—

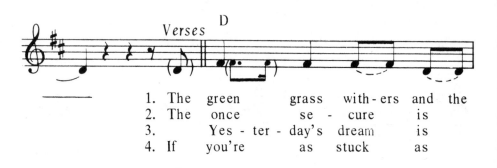

Verses D

———
1. The   green   grass with - ers and the
2. The   once   se - cure   is
3.   Yes - ter - day's dream   is
4. If   you're   as   stuck   as

Ps 90: 5-6
2 Co 3:18
Heb 1:10-12
Jas 1:17

flow - ers wilt. Cleansed is the one who was
now in spin. Some want out and
dead and gone. To - mor - row's hope is
old ce - ment, That life can't budge and

rid - den with guilt. ———— The sea - sons shift but
oth - ers want in. ———— You're tired of run-ning but you
draw - ing us on. ———— Some in - sist they
love can't dent. ———— You bet-ter start pray-ing and

is that strange? If you can't stay the same ————
can't stand still. If you don't move ————
just can't change. They seek a sta - bil - i - ty
pray - ing hard That there's some - bod - y left ————

———— then you've got to change. ————
———— then no - bod - y will. ————
———— that's out of their range. ————
———— in your own back yard. ————

rit.

same.

30/ Song Of Loveliness

Words and Music by
Sister Miriam Therese Winter

Reflectively

I watched a
1. hill burst in - to Spring.—
2. mo - ments turned to gold. —
3. A - pril leaves are gone. —

——— I heard a val - ley ring with mu -
——— I spoke of things my heart had
——There is no crutch for me to

sic.—— I saw my Mas - ter com - ing
nev - er told.—— My Mas - ter walked a - long with
lean up - on.——Some - times my Mas - ter does not

home in ear - ly eve - ning.———— He heard me
me in ear - ly eve - ning.———— He heard my
come in ear - ly eve - ning.———— And still I

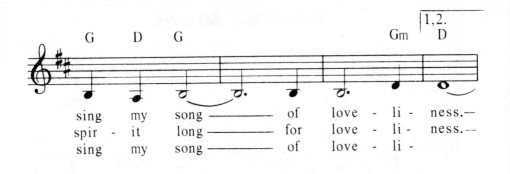

sing my song ———— of love - li - ness.—
spir - it long ———— for love - li - ness.—
sing my song ———— of love - li -

—2. Then all my ness. ——— And still I
—3. Now all the

sing my song of love - li - ness. ———

Song 2: 10-13; 3: 1-2

31/ The Sower

Words and Music by
Sister Miriam Therese Winter

Lively

Sow - er went out to sow his seed. Sing a - men,

al - le - lu! Sowed the wheat a - mong the weed, al - le - lu!

Some fell a - way and some took root, Yield - ed a hun - dred-

fold of fruit. Be - lieve in the word of the Lord.

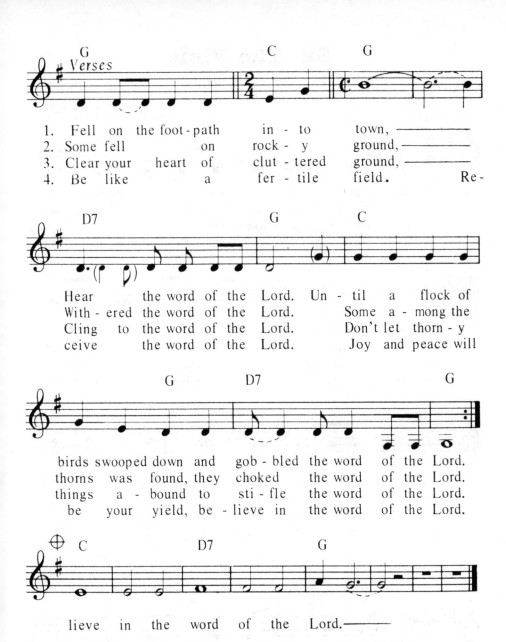

Verses

1. Fell on the foot-path in-to town, ————
2. Some fell on rock-y ground, ————
3. Clear your heart of clut-tered ground, ————
4. Be like a fer-tile field. Re-

Hear the word of the Lord. Un-til a flock of
With-ered the word of the Lord. Some a-mong the
Cling to the word of the Lord. Don't let thorn-y
ceive the word of the Lord. Joy and peace will

birds swooped down and gob-bled the word of the Lord.
thorns was found, they choked the word of the Lord.
things a-bound to sti-fle the word of the Lord.
be your yield, be-lieve in the word of the Lord.

lieve in the word of the Lord.————

Mt 13:3-23/Mk 4:3-20/Lk 8:4-15

32/ The Visit

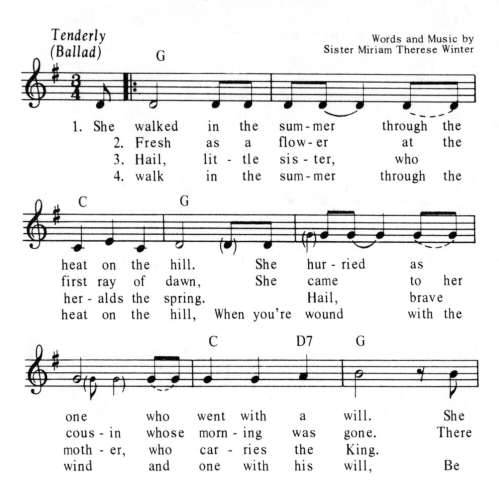

Tenderly
(Ballad)

Words and Music by
Sister Miriam Therese Winter

1. She walked in the sum-mer through the heat on the hill. She hur-ried as one who went with a will. She
2. Fresh as a flow-er at the first ray of dawn, She came to her cous-in whose morn-ing was gone. There
3. Hail, lit-tle sis-ter, who her-alds the spring. Hail, brave moth-er, who car-ries the King.
4. walk in the sum-mer through the heat on the hill, When you're wound with the wind and one with his will, Be

danced in the sun-light when the day was
leaped a lit-tle child in the an-cient
Hail to the mo-ment be - neath your
brave with the bur-den you are blessed to

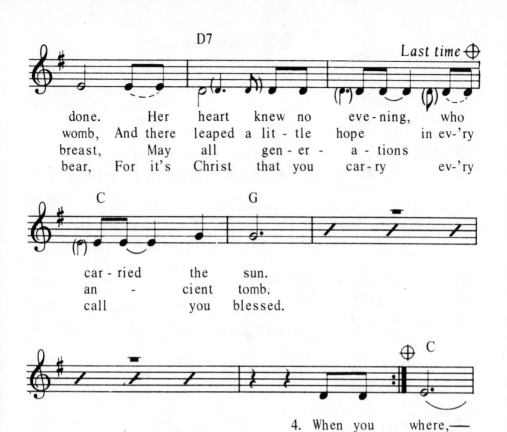

D7

Last time ⊕

done.   Her   heart   knew   no   eve - ning,   who
womb,   And   there   leaped   a   lit - tle   hope   in ev-'ry
breast,   May   all   gen - er -   a - tions
bear,   For   it's   Christ   that   you   car - ry   ev-'ry

C   **G**

car - ried   the   sun.
an -   cient   tomb.
call   you   blessed.

⊕ **C**

4. When you   where,——

D7   **G**   **C**   **G**
                   rit.

—— ev - 'ry - where,—— ev - 'ry - where.————

Lk 1:39-56

33/ John

Words and Music by
Sister Miriam Therese Winter

Dramatically

1. What did you go in - to the des - ert to see,
2. What did you go in - to the des - ert to see,
3. Are you the pro - phet, are you He who is to come?

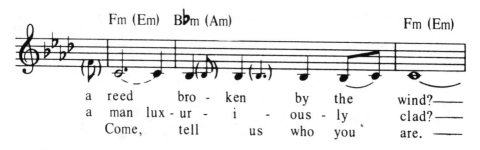

a reed bro - ken by the wind?——
a man lux - ur - i - ous - ly clad?——
Come, tell us who you are. ——

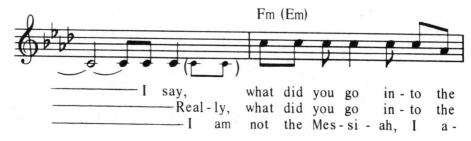

—————————— I say, what did you go in - to the
——————————Real - ly, what did you go in - to the
——————————I am not the Mes - si - ah, I a-

des - ert to see? A man of fire who be-
des - ert to hear? A her - ald's voice ring - ing
wait Him too, I'm un - wor - thy to loos - en the

* for chords in parenthesis capo 1.

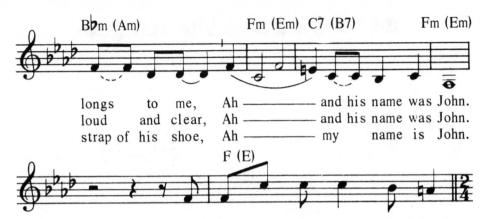

longs to me, Ah ——————— and his name was John.
loud and clear, Ah ——————— and his name was John.
strap of his shoe, Ah ——————— my name is John.

A voice in the wild - er - ness,

Let it be heard, ——————————— Pre -

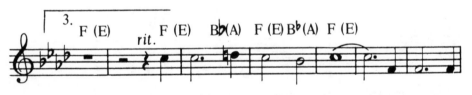

par - ing a way in the world for the Word.

Be - hold the Lamb of God,—— The man I

told you of.—— Be - hold the man I love. ——

Mt 3: 1-6, 11; 11: 7-10
Mk 1: 2-8   57
Jn 1: 6, 29-30

34/ Seek First the Kingdom

Words and Music by
Sister Miriam Therese Winter

Lively

Seek first the King-dom of Heav-en——— and all the

rest will fall in line.——— Give God His due and God will

give back to you, Turn your wa-ter in-to wine.———

1. Some folk are mon - ey mad, Go a - bout
2. Some folk are bare - ly fed, Beg - ging their
3. Some folk are nei - ther - nor; Life rush - es

Mt 6:33
Lk 6:24-25
Jn 2:9

rich - ly clad, Seek - ing the rain - bow's end.——
crust of bread From dawn to set - ting sun.——
by their door, Leav - ing them far be - hind.——

—— I tell you, God's sure to leave be-hind
—— I tell you, God will give lib - er - ty
—— I tell you, jump in and join the fight,

all who are not in - clined to treat the poor as
To those in pov - er - ty, A feast to ev - 'ry-
Stand up for what is right, with heart and hands and

friend.———— wa - ter in - to wine.————
one. ————
mind. ————

35/ I Built a Garden

Words and Music by
Sister Miriam Therese Winter

Gently

1. I built a gar - den and plant-ed my vines.— I dreamed of tast - ing the choic-est of wines. I sent my Son when the har - vest was full. My gar - den, my Son,——— were tram - pled. Green was my gar - den when first I came down.
2. friend - ship and plant-ed my vines.— I dreamed of tast - ing the choic-est of wines. I sent my Spir - it when the har - vest was full. My friend-ship, my Spir - it, were tram - pled. Green was my friend - ship when first I came down.
3. world and I plant-ed my vines.— I dreamed of tast - ing the choic-est of wines. I sent my Son when the har - vest was full. My world and my Son,——— were tram - pled. Green was my wor - ld when first I came down.

Is 5:1-7
Mt 21:33-46

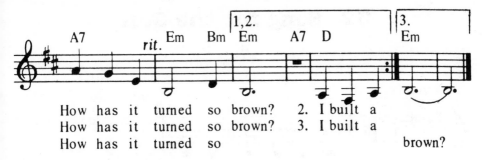

How has it turned so brown? 2. I built a
How has it turned so brown? 3. I built a
How has it turned so   brown?

36/ Night

Words and music by
Sister Miriam Therese Winter

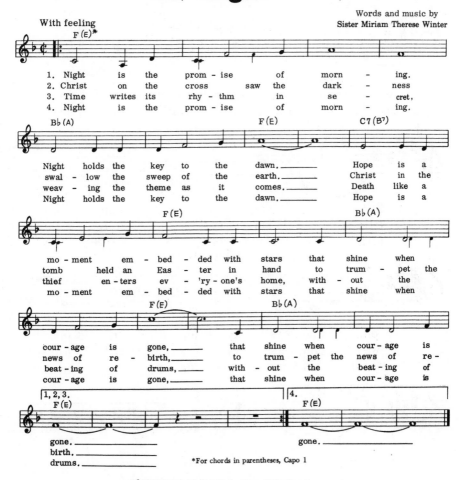

With feeling

F (E)*

1. Night   is   the   prom - ise   of   morn   –   ing.
2. Christ   on   the   cross   saw   the   dark   –   ness
3. Time   writes   its   rhy - thm   in   se   –   cret,
4. Night   is   the   prom - ise   of   morn   –   ing.

Bb (A)   F (E)   C7 (B7)

Night   holds   the   key   to   the   dawn. _____   Hope   is   a
swal - low   the   sweep   of   the   earth. _____   Christ   in   the
weav - ing   the   theme   as   it   comes. _____   Death   like   a
Night   holds   the   key   to   the   dawn. _____   Hope   is   a

F (E)   Bb (A)

mo - ment   em - bed - ded   with   stars   that   shine   when
tomb   held   an   Eas - ter   in   hand   to   trum - pet   the
thief   en - ters   ev - 'ry - one's   home,   with - out   the
mo - ment   em - bed - ded   with   stars   that   shine   when

F (E)   Bb (A)

cour - age   is   gone, _____   that   shine   when   cour - age   is
news   of   re - birth, _____   to   trum - pet   the   news   of   re -
beat - ing   of   drums, _____   with - out   the   beat - ing   of
cour - age   is   gone, _____   that   shine   when   cour - age   is

1, 2, 3.   4.
F (E)   F (E)

gone. _____   gone. _____
birth. _____
drums. _____   *For chords in parentheses, Capo 1

Job 11:16-18
Ps 30:5
2 Pet 1:19

37/ Song for the Sun

Words and Music by
Sister Miriam Therese Winter

Moderately

1. This is a song for the sun that's dy-ing.
2. This is a song for the day that's dy-ing,
3. This is a song for a love un-dy-ing,

—— Red are the tears that stain the
—— And for the dreams it could not
—— And for a faith they can-not

hill. —— This is a song for the
fill. —— This is a song for the
kill. —— This is a song for a

one who is ly-ing still in the
way it is try-ing still to be
world that is cry-ing to sleep in his

sun. ——
day. —— will.

Ps 104:19   Mt 16:2-3
Is 60:19-20

38/ Lift Up Your Hearts

Words and Music by
Sister MIRIAM THERESE WINTER

Moderately, with zest

Chorus:

Lift up your hearts, lift them high, up to the Lord.

Sing your song, loud and long. All you peo-ples, praise the Lord.

Verse:
1. My
2. A
3. How

Rock and my Re - fuge, _____ for you . I long.
light to all na - tions, _____ dis - pel our night.
hap - py your peo - ple _____ whose hearts have heard

To
Your
the

you I pray at break of day _____ and sing a new
love will find our hearts are blind. _____ Come bring a new
won - der of your law of love. _____ You speak a new

1. 2.
song.
light.

3.
Word. _____

Last Chorus:

Lift up your hearts, lift them high, up to the Lord.

rit.

Sing your song, loud and long. All you peo - ples, praise the Lord.

Ps 5:2-3
Ps 18:2
Ps 67:5
Lam 3:41
Jn 13:34
Rev 21:22-26

39/ Ballad of the Seasons

Words and Music by
Sister MIRIAM THERESE WINTER

Eccles 3: 1-8

40/ Let There Be Peace

Prayerfully

Words and Music by
Sister MIRIAM THERESE WINTER

Chorus:

Let there be peace in your dwell - ing. ___

Let there be peace this day. ___ Peace is the

gift that I of - fer, ___ that no - one can take a -

Verse:

way. ___ So let their wars and their ter - rors re -
I will not leave you an or - phan a -
Peace to the towns and the cit - ies of

sound. ___ You, my child, are on cer - tain ground.
lone. ___ You are the child I claim as my own.
earth, ___ peace to the land that I loved in - to birth,

Don't let your heart be a - fraid. ___ Don't let your
You hold the key to my heart. ___ You hold the
so that your joy may be full. ___ So that your

1. 2. 3. *D.C. al fine*

heart be a - fraid. ___
key to my heart. ___
joy may be full. ___

Lk 10:3-5
Jn 14:1,18,27; 15:11; 20:26

41/ Help My Unbelief

Words and Music by
Sister MIRIAM THERESE WINTER

Chorus:

Lord, I be-lieve,— help my un-be-lief. I would not grieve, take a-way my grief. The Lord is pre-sent, run to re-ceive— him.— His word is spo-ken, let us be-lieve him.—

Verse:

His are the moun-tains, his the lands.
To you, O Lord,— I lift my soul.
Who would be healed— must first be-lieve.

All of cre-a-tion is clap-ping its hands.— There's mus-ic in the wind and
My bro-ken spir-it, make it whole.— I stum-ble through the dark and
We who would give _____ must first re-ceive.— We live each mo-ment

danc-ing in the stream. There's love all a-bout me, or
wan-der through the day. Your love has told me, this
as it's willed. Our emp-ti-ness will one

1.2.
so it seems.
is the way.

3.
day be filled.

Last Chorus:

Lord, I be-lieve,— help my un-be-lief. I would not grieve, take a-way my grief. The Lord is pre-sent, run to re-ceive— him. His word is spo-ken, let us be-lieve, His word is spo-ken, let us be-lieve, His word is spo-ken, let us be-lieve him. _____

Ps 86:4
Is 55:12
Mk 9:23-24

42/ Shout the Good News

Words and Music by
Sister MIRIAM THERESE WINTER

With zest

Go

Chorus:

out and shout the Good News,_____ loose the chains of the deaf and dumb.__

_____ Tell the whole wide wait - ing world:_____

Last time
to Coda

_____ The King-dom of God is come._____ 4. The

Verse:

1. Heal the sick in ev - 'ry land,_ give the help - less heart a help - ing hand._
2. Go to the cor - ners of the earth,_ bring the Christ in ev - 'ry - one to birth._
3. Com - fort, en - cour - age, and con - sole;_ lift the bro - ken spir - it, make it whole..
4. fox has a hole, the bird its nest,_ but the friends of God no place to rest.__ The

Guide the blind, sup - port the la me._____ let the
Shout His mes - sage, sing His word,_____ and
Put your hand up - on the plough,_____ it
fields are full but the work - ers few;_____

Tell them who sent you and why you came._____ 2. Go
prom - is - es of Christ be heard._____ 3. Go
don't look back, your hour is now._____ 4. Go
all de - pends on me and you._____

___ come.___

Mt 28:19
Lk 4:18-19; 9:58,62; 10:1-9

43/ Spirit of the Lord

Words and Music by
Sister MIRIAM THERESE WINTER

1. The Spir - it hov - ered o - ver the wa - ter, and the world was born. The Spir - it hov - ered o - ver the dark - ness, and it was morn - ing. Deep in the world the Spir - it stood, smiled on the world, for it was good. Spir - it of the Lord, come, we sing.

2. The Spir - it hov - ered o - ver a maid - en, and a King was born. The Spir - it hov - ered o - ver a sealed tomb, and it was morn - ing. The veil of the tem - ple was torn in two, with - out an - y warn - ing the old was new. Spir - it of the Lord, come, we sing.

3. The Spir - it hov - ers o - ver cre - a - tion, and the world is re - born. The Spir - it hov - ers o - ver our dark - ness, and it is morn - ing. The Spir - it comes with a brand new spring, re - new - ing, re - fresh - ing ev - 'ry - thing. Spir - it of the Lord, come, we

Spir - it of the Lord, come, We hun - ger for a whole new spring. Our wear - y hearts to you we bring. Come, Spir - it of the Lord, we sing.

Gen 1:1-2
Ps 104:30
Mt 28:2
Mk 15:38
Lk 1:35
Acts 1:8

44/ How High the Sky

Words and Music by
Sister MIRIAM THERESE WINTER

Chorus: With gusto

How high the sky, _____ how wide the earth, how deep the sea. _____ But nei - ther height nor depth, nor death nor an - y - thing can sep - ar - ate the love of Christ from me. _____

Last time

1. Let
2. Let
3. One

Verse:

love be the cor - ner - stone on which your build - ing stands. Let
love be the root and foun - da - tion of your life. Let
can on - ly har - vest what ev - er one sows. If

love be the bound-'ry sur - round - ing your lands. Let love be the
love be the flow - er-ing of gen - tle-ness in strife. The Fa - ther sent His
we would reap love, we see that it grows. We sow in the

lode-stone that leads you from a - far. Let love be ev - 'ry - thing you
prom - ise of which you are a - part, when love takes hold with - in your
Spir - it a la - bor of love. God gives the in - crease from a -

are. _____
heart. _____
bove. _____

me. _____

Rm 8:35-39
I Co 3:6
2 Co 9:6-8
Eph 2:19-22; 3:17-19
I Thess 1:3

45/ Runnin'

Words and Music by
Sister MIRIAM THERESE WINTER

Chorus:

Run-nin', _____ run-nin' a-way. _____ Run to to-mor-row, _____ run from to-day. _____ Ev-'ry-bod-y's run-nin', _____ right or wrong. _____ 'Cept the just in the strength of the Lord go walk-ing a-long.

Verse:

1. Run from au-tumn 'cause the leaves turn brown. Run, run 'cause your won-der-ful dream world's a-tum-bl-ing down. _____
2. Run from liv-ing 'cause you just don't dare. Run, run from — lone-li-ness, emp-ti-ness and — des-pair. _____
3. Keep on run-ning and you soon will find, your trou-bles all fol-low but the good is — left — be-hind. _____

long. _____ The just stand still and in the strength of the Lord grow strong. _____

Ps 89:15-17
Ps 92:12
Jon 1:3
1 Co 9:24

46/ If You Look

Words and Music by
Sister MIRIAM THERESE WINTER

Moderately slow

1. If you look ver-y close, you'll see wind on the top of the hill.
2. look ver-y close, you'll see clouds in the clear-est of skies.
3. look ver-y close, you'll see Christ on the crest of the sea.

If you look ver-y close, you'll see love un-der-neath what I will.
If you look ver-y close, you'll see hun-ger in so man-y eyes.
If you look ver-y close, you'll see Christ en-com-pass-ing me.

If you lis-ten, you'll hear a song when the cit-y is still.
There's a dawn ev-'ry day, but it's al-ways a love-ly sur-prise.
In-side ev-'ry seed is a flow-er that longs to be free.

Chorus:
We look and look, but so sel-dom do we see.
We watch and wait, but so sel-dom un-der-stand.
We look and look, but so sel-dom do we see.

Last time to Coda
We love, but af-ter all, what do you know of me?
We reach, — but how of-ten ex-tend — a com-fort-ing hand.
We love, but af-ter all,

2. If you
3. If you

rit.
how did this hap-pen to be?

Is 6:9/Mt 13:14
2 Co 4:18

*For chords in parentheses, Capo 1

47/ Praise God

Words and Music by
Sister MIRIAM THERESE WINTER

With gusto

Chorus:

Praise God, the Fa - ther, praise and glo - ri - fy the Son. Joined to-
geth - er in the Spir - it, in the Spi - rit we are one.

fine

1. Praise God, the Fa - ther, who has loved us, ev - 'ry
2. Thank you, Lord Je - sus, for the bless - ings of this
3. Born of the Spir - it, we are chil - dren who are

one. He has prom - ised us a king - dom when our time on earth is
day, for dy - ing to re - deem us and for show - ing us the
free, free to choose to love each oth - er, and we love our lib - er -

done. We as chil - dren of the prom - ise own the fat - ness of the
way. You have gone home to the Fa - ther to pre - pare for us a
ty. Man - y gifts we have been giv - en which the Spir - it has out -

land, and we live now in the shel - ter of the shad - ow of his
place. You have raised to ho - ly splen - dor the con - di - tion of our
poured for our build - ing a foun - da - tion in the bod - y of the

1, 2.
hand.
race.

3.
Lord.

D.C. al fine

Ps 91:1
Jn 14:2-3
Rm 8:15-17
I Co 12:4-7
Eph 1:3; 4:4

48/ A Long Night

Words and Music by
Sister MIRIAM THERESE WINTER

Brightly

Chorus:

It's a long night, _____ it's a long _____ day. _____ Come share my ta - ble, come stay and break bread. _____ The day is spent ___ and the road a - head ___ is a long _____ way. _____

fine

Verse:

1. Two ___ men ___ went walk - ing ___ and talk - ing ___ a - bout Him who had ris - en ___ from the dead. _____ They were joined by a stran - ger, and when they reached _____ their vil - lage they said: _____ It's a

2. The stran - ger told a sto - ry. ___ He told them ___ a - bout Him who had ris - en ___ from the dead. _____ Their hearts burned with - in them when they heard _____ the things that he said: _____

3. Two men went walk - ing ___ and talk - ing ___ with Him who had ris - en ___ from the dead. _____ And sud - den - ly their eyes were o - pened at the break - ing of ___ the bread. _____

Lk 24:13-35

49/ Who Is My Neighbor?

Moderately

Words and Music by
Sister MIRIAM THERESE WINTER

Lk 10:29-37

50/ Don't Be Afraid

Words and Music by
Sister MIRIAM THERESE WINTER

With intensity

Lam 2:19
Mt 14:26-31
Mk 10:45
Lk 21:11; 23:33

51/ So Full of Song

Words and Music by
Sister MIRIAM THERESE WINTER

Lightly

1. I'm so full of song I must sing like a
2. so full of joy I must dance like a
3. so full of love I must run to your

bird. I have been touched by His won-der-ful
child! He gave me a gift when the night wind was
needs, so full of love I must show it in

Word, Touched by a mes-sage so sim-ple and
wild, gave me a gift I might claim as my
deeds. I live in God, oh, but how can this

strong; of this is my song.
own, a love that has grown.
be? He lives in

2. I'm
3. I'm

me! 4. I'm so full of song I must

sing like a bird, sing sweet-er songs than the world ev-er

heard. My hap-py heart is the hall of a King, of

this do I sing.

Lk 1:39-49
Gal 2:20

52/ Beatitudes

Words and Music by
Sister MIRIAM THERESE WINTER

Reflectively

1. Hap-py are the poor, they shall in-her-it the
2. Hap-py are the mer-ci-ful, they shall have mer-cy in re-
3. Hap-py is the one who has learned to han-dle

land. Hap-py those who know what sor-row means,—
turn. Hap-py are the ut-ter-ly sin-cere,—
blame. Hap-py those who are ill-treat-ed for—

they shall un-der-stand. Hap-py those who hold no
God is their sole con-cern. Hap-py those who die for
the glo-ry of my name, for in this and ev-'ry

claims, we'll put the world in-to their hand.
peace, They die that all of us may learn.
age, we treat the pro-phets just the same.

Hap-py those who hun-ger and thirst for good-ness,
Hap-py those who suf-fer the scourge of ha-tred,
So I say be glad, you my friends, and thank-ful,

for they shall be sat-is-fied.
whose free-dom is de-nied.
for great is your re-ward.

Last time to Coda

Hap-py— are you who dare to think and—
Hap-py— are you who dare to think and—
Hap-py— are you who dare to think and—

do, who dare to have
do, who dare to have

tried.
died.

do, and be like the Lord.

rit.

Mt 5: 3-12/Lk 6:20-23

53/ Ballad of the Women

Words and Music by
Sister MIRIAM THERESE WINTER

Mt 25:1-13

not!"   burns.

Last Chorus:

Hur-ry and light your lamps, Chris-tians, Soon the Lord will be re-turn-ing.

Watch and wait. It's get-ting late. Be sure when he comes that your lamps are burn-ing!

54/ Children of the Lord

Words and Music by
Sister MIRIAM THERESE WINTER

Simply

1. We are chil-dren of the Lord,
2. Fa - ther, hear the song we sing,
3. Sing, O chil-dren, to the Lord.

ga - thered here to pray to - geth - er.
as we bring our world be - fore you.
All the world is hushed and wait - ing,

We are one with - in his love.
Soon your Word will sow the seed,
as we lift our hearts a - bove,

This we know we're cer - tain of.
sow your strength with - in our need.
sim - ply liv - ing in his

love.

Mt 13:23
Jn 1:12
Rm 8:16,19
1 Jn 3:1

55/ Dying Just the Same

Words and Music by
Sister MIRIAM THERESE WINTER

Lively

1. Oh, they im - pri - soned
2. Oh, they stoned
3. Oh, they be - head - ed

Paul___ and put Pe - ter in - to chains. All of
Ste - phen and put Law-rence on___ the grill. E - ven
John___ and put An-drew on___ a cross. On our

us must pre - pare to suf-fer pains, if we would live for the
we must___ go a-gainst our will, if we would live for the
part, pre - pare to suf-fer loss, if we would live for the

Lord and la - bor for his glo - ry. It's a new, new
Lord and la - bor for his glo - ry. It's a new, new
Lord and la - bor for his glo - ry. It's a new, new

age, but the same old sto - ry.___ *fine*
age, but the same old sto - ry.___
age, but the same old sto - ry.___

1. Live for the mo - ment,___
2. Don't be dis - cour - aged if
3. All must suf - fer,___

come what may. Do your best and
things look grey. Lots of gra - ces
all must die. But more is asked of

go your way. The blood of mar - tyrs___
come this way. The blood of mar - tyrs___ is
you and I. The blood of mar - tyrs is the

built the chur-ch's name. We but die by in - ches, but we're
now as it was then. We who die with Je - sus___ will
seed of love, and the re - sur - rec - tion is a

dy - ing just the same.
sure - ly rise a - gain.
fact we're cer - tain of. *(Repeat: "Oh, they imprisoned Paul.." to fine.)*

Mk 6:24, 27
Acts 7:58-59; 12:6; 16:24
Rm 6:5
Rev 17:6

56/ Love Each Other

Words and Music by
Sister MIRIAM THERESE WINTER

With feeling

1. If you don't love each oth-er,___ don't call up-on my
2. If you should shine like some-one who is the peo-ple's

name. If you don't love each oth-er,___ you're play-ing a
choice. If you should man - age mar-vels,___ what rea-son to re-

game. My chil - dren, you sought me in your loss.___
joice. My chil - dren, who hun-ger for ac - claim,___

___ I lis - tened,___ and you hung me on a Cross.
they hailed me,___ yet they hung me just the

same.

3. If you should have all know-ledge,___ and peo-ple deem you
4. If you don't seek my king - dom, you will not hear it's

wise. If you should see your schemes grow
call. If you don't love my ways, you

great be - fore your eyes. My chil - dren, be
may not love at all. My chil - dren, my

care - ful in your play,___ lest in-
love is o - pen wide.

rit. 2nd time

te - gri - ty for - ev - er walk a - way.
Love, and you'll find your - self in - side.

I Co 13: 1-13
I Jn 3: 16-18; 4: 7-12

57/ Seven Times

Words and Music by
Sister MIRIAM THERESE WINTER

Moderately

Chorus:

Sev - en times, Lord, _____ Sev - en

times. Shall we for - give each oth - er _____ sev - en

times? _____

Verses:

1. "Pe - ter, do you know this man? Is He your mas - ter? Tell us why you ran." "I swear, this man I do not know!" Then _ sud-den - ly, a cock be - gan to crow.

2. "Wom - an, take us to your man. Who is your hus - band? Tell us, if you can. Your se - cret sins _ are all known." "Who is guilt - less, let him cast a stone."

3. Je - sus, hang-ing on a tree. We hung our God for all the world to see. Then He cried out for me and you: "For - give them, they know not what they do."

Last Chorus:

Sev - en times sev - en, sev - en times. Let us for - give each oth- - er _____ ev - 'ry time. _

ritard.

Mt 18:21-22; 26:74-75
Lk 23:34
Jn 4:16-18; 8:7

58/ Loved by the Lord

Words and Music by
Sister MIRIAM THERESE WINTER

Lyrically

1. Whose are the hands that han – dle the hands of a
2. Whose are the tears that fall on the feet of a
3. What are these hands that they reach to the hearts of the

King? Whose are the hands of
King? Whose are the tears of
poor? What are these hands that

which ev – 'ry proph – et shall sing? The
which all of his – t'ry will sing? The
touch the torn and un – sure? They be –

hands of a wom – an loved by the Lord,
tears of a wom – an loved by the Lord,
long to a wom – an loved by the Lord,

a wom – an to whom all
the tears of a wom – an for the
they be – long to a heart whose

A rit. last time only

time has looked toward.
God she a – dored.
love is out – poured.

Much was she
Much was for –
Much are we

giv – en for great was her love.
giv – en for great was her love.
giv – en when great is our

3. love.

Lk 1:28; 7:37-38, 44-47

59/ Hear My Call

Words and Music by
Sister MIRIAM THERESE WINTER

Moderately slow

1. Hear my call, _____
2. Hear my cry, _____

God _____ of mer - cy.
God _____ of mer cy.

Hear my call _____ and an - swer my plea. _____
Wa - ters come _____ to cov - er my soul. _____

In the night _____
Strength is poured _____

___ I cry to you, _____
___ up - on the ground. _____

sing my song _____ the whole night
Threat - 'ning ter - rors ring me

through. _____ Still at dawn, _____
round. _____ Be be - side _____

___ my song goes on and on. _____
___ me, Lord, to guard and

1. Em

2. Em

guide. _____

84

3. Hear my call, _____ God _____ of mer - cy. Be pro - tec - tion when I'm a - lone. _____ Keep my foot - steps from the snare. _____ I'll not fear _____ when you are there. _____ Come and keep _____ a vig - il while I sleep. _____ You know the way is steep, _____ and yet my trust is deep, _____ in - to your love I leap, _____ and I'm at peace. _____

rit.

Ps 42:8   Ps 77:2
Ps 61:1   Ps 91:3,5-6
Ps 69:1-3,14-15

60/ God Speaks

Words and Music by
Sister MIRIAM THERESE WINTER

Chorus: *Rhythmically*

God spoke to Job in a whirl - wind.
The moun - tains trem - bled be - fore His face.
God spoke to Mo-ses in a cloud and there was fire _____ in the ho -ly place.
God speaks to me in the flash of a storm and in the warmth of His grace.

Verses

1. I call on my Lord ___ in my hour of need. I cry to my God, ___ come ___
2. I call on my Lord ___ for my dai - ly bread. I cry to my God ___ and ___
3. I call on my Lord ___ to send His peace. I cry to my God ___ when I

pay me ___ heed.
I am ___ fed.
need re - lease.

He

Out of the dark - ness He will lead me, with His own flesh ___ and ___
dwells ___ in ___ me, I am re - mind - ed. Still I am dumb ___ and my
Out of the dark, ___ I know He'll hear me. Some-times I feel ___ His ___

blood He'll feed me. grace.
eyes are blind - ed.
pres - ence near me.

Ex 19:16-19   Ps 4:3
I Kings 19:11-12   Jn 6:53
Job 38:1   I Co 3:16

61/ Thank You For Today

Words and Music by
Sister MIRIAM THERESE WINTER

Song Refrain Emphatically

Thank you for to-day. Hear us as we pray.

(Harmony)

Thank you for to-day. Hear us as we

Give your Son to ev-'ry-one and stay _____ near.

pray. _____ Give your Son and stay _____ near.

Verses

Lis-ten one and all; walk wor-thy_ of your
All be of one mind; be mer-ci-ful, lov-ing,

call. Some are called to sing. Oth-ers are called to
kind. Com-fort those who grieve. Share_ what you re-

bring God's heal-ing Word, 'till all have heard the
ceive. Love one an-oth-er as sis-ter and broth-er and to-

mir-a-cles of which we sing: Our God lives and He
geth-er seek the things a-bove. Our God takes ev-'ry-

gives and gives to ev-'ry-one, ev-'ry-thing.
thing He makes, trans-form-ing it with His love.

Ps 118:29
Rm 12:9-18
I Co 12:4-11
Eph 4:1-13
Phil 2:2

62/ Wonderful

Moderately

Words and Music by
Sister MIRIAM THERESE WINTER

Now the emp - ti - ness of a - ges pro - claims the prom - ised
Streams will wash a - way the des - ert as He goes pass - ing

birth. Hope to help un - hap - py hearts. Love to light the
by. Those in need will turn to Him. He will hear their

earth. And He shall be called ___ Won - der - ful! ___
cry. And He shall be called ___ Won - der - ful! ___

He shall be called Peace. For to us a Son has been
He shall be called Peace. He will lead His flock like a

giv - en, to us the Lord is born. He will gov - ern with
shep - herd and call us each by name. He will walk in the

jus - tice and joy, con - so - ling those who mourn. And
fa - vor of God, and we ___ shall do the same. And

He shall be called ___ Com - for - ter. ___ He shall be called Peace.
He shall be called ___ Com - for - ter. ___ He shall be called Peace.

Is 9:6-7; 35:1-7; 40:10-11; 43:1

63/ Child of Morning

Words and Music by
Sister MIRIAM THERESE WINTER

Lightly

1. Sing a song to the
2. Sing a song to the
3. Sing a song to the

Child of Morn - ing, sing for the King__ is com - ing.__
Child of Sor - row, sing for the dream_ re - turn - ing.__
Child of Morn - ing, sing for the child__ that's cry - ing.__

To the maid to whom he was born, sing to her brave be -
Love to - day and laugh to - mor - row, sing for the things we're
Big black head - lines scream a __ warn - ing... sing for the dead and

com - ing. Sing of a peace he will bring a - gain,
learn - ing. Love, the in - vis - i - ble,__ now ap - pears, with __
dy - ing. The Child of the Morn - ing__ must be slain, yet a

peace and fel - low - ship. Praise him then! Sing glo - ry to
time to be ten - der and time for tears. Sing glo - ry to
sliv - er of light __ and hope re - main. Sing glo - ry to

1, 2.

3.

God in the high - est.
God in the high - est.
God in the high - est.

Mt 2:16-18
Lk 2:7,14
Col 1:15
Rev 22:16

64/ Christmas Ballad

Words and Music by
Sister MIRIAM THERESE WINTER

Reflectively

1. Jo - seph and Ma - ry were liv - ing in Ga - li - lee,
2. set out at once, though the trip would be rough, they could see.
3. When they ar - rived, Ma - ry knew that her mo - ment had come.
4. So in the dirt and the damp and the dark of a cave,

when Cae - sar de - mand - ed a cen - sus by his de -
They made no com - plaint, for they knew this was how it must
Jo - seph went search - ing for shel - ter still of - fered to
took flesh all the love and the life that our God e - ver

cree.
be.   They had to tra - vel to
some.   Ma - ry went hap - pi - ly
gave....   a beau - ti - ful burst of a
           But stran - gers were sus - pect and

Beth - le - hem, which was a ve - ry long way for them, and
from the start. She car - ried the love light in her heart, for
hearts were hard. The hopes and the homes of the world were barred, and
bril - liant sun, a once - in - a - life - time, seen by none, for

Ma - ry would soon, so soon, de - li - ver her child.
Ma - ry would soon, so soon, de - li - ver her child.
Ma - ry would soon, so soon, de - li - ver her child.
                                          2. They

rallantando

Ma - ry had qui - et - ly, sim - ply de - li - vered her child.

Lk 2:1-7

65/ Sing of Birth

Words and Music by
Sister MIRIAM THERESE WINTER

Lyrically

1. On a cold and lone - ly night in the hills of a land called
2. In a sim - ple cat - tle shed in the hills of a land called
3. You who are born of pov - er - ty in a mo - dern town or

Ju - da,___ there shone a star so big and bright, that
Ju - da,___ on a straw - filled man - ger bed, the
ghet - to...___ God al - lows that this should be. He

all the fields re - flect - ed light, and shep - herds mar - velled
Son of God lay down His head. A king chose com - mon
chose to make you just as He. He'll come a - gain to

at the sight and sang their al - le - lu - ia.
ways in - stead! O sing an al - le - lu - ia.
set you free, so sing your al - le - lu - ia.

Sing, you peo - ple, Sing of birth. Christ our God has come to earth.

Sing, you peo - ple, Sing of birth. Christ, our God, has come to earth!

Lk 2:4-20

66/ He Comes

Words and Music by
Sister MIRIAM THERESE WINTER

Rhythmically *Or Key of C, as in Verses 4 & 5

1. Who do you bear in your heart, Ma - ry, who?
2. What is the Sav - ior's name, Ma - ry, what?
3. When will the Sav - ior come, Ma - ry, when?

Who do you bear in your heart, Ma - ry, who?
What is the Sav - ior's name, Ma - ry, what? His
When will the Sav - ior come, Ma - ry, when? When

In my heart I bear a Son, the God and friend of ev' - ry - one. He
name is Je - sus, Christ and Lord. In Him sal - va - tion is re - stored. He
love is cold and hope has died, He'll come as love per - son - i - fied. He

comes to save His peo - ple from their sins.
comes to save His peo - ple from their sins.
comes to save His peo - ple from their

sins.

4. Where will the Sav - ior be
5. Why does the Sav - ior

born, Ma - ry, where? Where will the Sav - ior be
come, Ma - ry, why? Why does the Sav - ior

born, Ma - ry, where? He's born of you, He's
come, Ma - ry, why? This is the won - drous

born of me. Who wel - comes Him, there He will be. He comes to save His
mys - ter - y, to which love is the root and key. He comes to save His

92

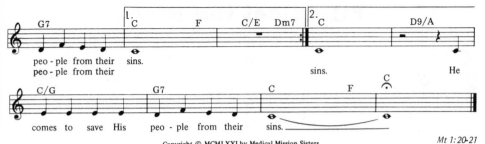

peo - ple from their sins.
peo - ple from their sins. He
comes to save His peo - ple from their sins.

Mt 1: 20-21

67/ In The Beginning

Words and Music by
Sister MIRIAM THERESE WINTER

Reverently

1. In the be - gin - ning was the Word: the Word was
2. And then a man was sent by God, He was a
3. And so the Word was in the world, with His own
4. And by the will of God Him - self, the Word was

with God, And the Word was God.
wit - ness, His name was John.
peo - ple, His own do - main.
with us, the Word was flesh. The

Through Him all things came to be, all things had
He came as wit - ness to the light. He came that
world had its be - ing through the Word, and yet His
He lived a - mong us, side by side. We saw His

life in Him, and He was the light, the light in the
ev' - ry - one might be - lieve and sing of the
mes - sage was not heard, a - lone, un - known, re -
glo - ry far and wide. He touched our race,

Last time slowly

dark - ness of the night.
light en - light - en - ing.
ject - ed by His own. In the be - gin - ning was the Word.
full of truth and grace.

Jn 1:1-16

68/ Silent the Night

Words and Music by
Sister MIRIAM THERESE WINTER

Mt 2:1-2, 9-11
Lk 2:7

69/ Take Courage

Words and Music by
Sister MIRIAM THERESE WINTER

Strength - en all the wea - ry___ hands, stead - y

all the trem - bling knees. Say to all faint hearts, "Take

cour - age!"___ For He comes the Prince of Peace. Peace

1. The blind eyes shall be o - pened and the
2. A lit - tle child shall lead us from the
3. One morn - ing in a man - ger brought our

ears of the deaf un - sealed. The crook - ed shall be
dark - ness___ of the past. Though stub - born - ness im -
ex - ile___ to an end. The Lord came as a

straight-ened and the hid - den thoughts re - vealed.
pede us, we shall know a peace at last.
strang - er and be - came our sa - ving friend.

Is 9:6; 11:6; 35:3-6
Lk 2:7

70/ No Longer Alone

Words and Music by
Sister MIRIAM THERESE WINTER

Ps 29:3-4
Wis 18:14-15
Jn 1:9; 8:12; 14:15-21; 15:12-15

71/ O What a Happening!

Words and Music by
Sister MIRIAM THERESE WINTER

With feeling

1. On a dark day___ deep in De-cem-ber,___ grind-ing the pov-er-ty,
2. On a dark day___ deep in the pres-ent,___ grind-ing the lone-li-ness and

grey was the morn. On-ly the clean of heart still can re-mem-ber the
plight of the poor. On-ly the clean of heart dare to re-mem-ber, the

day and the mo-ment when Je-sus was born.
poor were His Gos-pel and their hope is sure.

O what a hap-pen-ing! Chris-tians re-joice! Lift up your hearts!

Lift up your voice! O what a hap-pen-ing! Love came to

birth ___ when Je-sus, our Sa-vior came to

1.
earth.
2.
earth. When Je-sus, our

Sa-vior came to earth. ___

Mt 5:8
Jn 1:14

72/ Peace Upon Earth

Words and Music by
Sister MIRIAM THERESE WINTER

Peace up - on earth is the prayer we
Life of the world, and a new be -
Glo - ry to God in His might and

of - fer. Peace was the prom - ise when Je - sus was
gin - ning, bright as a star - night when our light is
po - wer, once but a child as the Fa - ther had

born. Peace we have heard,
dim. His Word will live.
planned. Pray now that we

Peace is his
Hur - ry to
one day might

Word to this war - wea - ry, war - wor - ried world
give Him the whole of our lives, let us wel -
be but a mo - ment of peace cra - dled in

this morn.
come Him.
His hand.

Lk 2:14
Jn 6:33,51
I Pet 1:23-25

73/ Song of Glory

*(Group)   Lively   (All)   Words and Music by
                                                     D Sister MIRIAM THERESE WINTER

1. God's own Son has come to earth,   Glo - ry, glo - ry, sing,
2. All the love since time be - gan,
3. Praise to the God who sets us free.

glo - ry to God.   Cel - e - brate His won - der - ful birth.
Lives with - in this won - der - ful man.
Praise to the God who lets us be.

Glo - ry, glo - ry, sing,   glo - ry to God.   Hear the good news
                                               Ev - 'ry - thing that
                                               Praise to the Fa - ther

of this Word.   Glo - ry, glo - ry, sing,   glo - ry to God.
was and is,
and the Son.

Share the sound of hope we've heard,   Glo - ry, glo - ry, sing,
Finds new life in this love of his,
Praise to the Spir - it in ev - 'ry - one,

glo - ry to God.   God of love,   Glo - ry to God,   God of splen - dor,
                   God of earth,   God of peo - ple,
                   Let us sing,   Glo - ry to God,   sing His prai - ses,

Glo - ry to God,   God of life,   Glo - ry to God.
                   God of peace,
                   sing of peace,

                   3rd time
                   Slower
                   (All)

Glo - ry, glo - ry, sing, glo - ry to God.   Glo - ry, glo - ry, sing glo - ry to God.

*Can be sung in alternate sections.

Lk 2:10-14

74/ Song of Liberation

Key: Cm CAPO: 3rd Play Am

Words and music by
Sister Miriam Therese Winter

With intensity

Refrain

Shout _____ to ev - 'ry na-tion! Pro-claim in-teg-ri-ty

and lib-er-a-tion! Feed the hun-gry wher-ev-er they may be and

let the op-pressed go free, _____ free!

Verses *Lyrically*

1. You shall be called re - build - er of ru - ins,
2. You shall be like a well - wa - tered gar - den,
3. Your light shall rise like dawn in the dark - ness,
4. Jus - tice and peace will go then be - fore you,

make old foun - da - tions rise up strong. Mend - er of
a spring whose wa - ters won't run dry, giv - ing re -
and all your shad - ows shall shine like noon. All of your
God's glo - ry fol - low - ing close be - hind, swift - ly re -

breach - es, the Lord will be your song. _____
lief to des - ert wastes that cry. _____
wounds will feel his heal - ing soon. _____
spon - ding, "I'm here, not hard to find." _____

Isaiah 58

75/ How Shall I Sing

With feeling

Words and Music by
Sr. Miriam Therese Winter

REFRAIN

How _____ shall I sing _____ the Lord's _____ song in a strange land? What can I say? How shall I pray? Who, _____ who'll un - der - stand? _____ ___ who'll un - der - stand? ___

VERSES

1. Gone are the songs. Gone is the danc - ing. All that re - mains, so it seems, Is the pain of the prom-ise and our _____ dreams.

2. We hung up our harps. We si - lenced our mu - sic Un - til our chains and the sword Give ___ way to the day ___ of the ___ Lord.

to Verses | Final Ending

Repeat Refrain

Ps 137:1-6

76/ Jerusalem

Intro: Am   *With feeling*

Words and Music by
Sr. Miriam Therese Winter

1. Je - ru - sa-lem, _____

why   are your walls   so   high?

Why   do you wait   at   each   guard-ed   gate   and

cry? _____   When   will

your   cher - ished   ones,   your   stur - dy   young

sons   cease   to   die? _____

2. Je - ru - sa-lem, _____
3. Je - ru - sa-lem, _____
4. Je - ru - sa-lem, _____

des-tined   to   rise   and   fall.
shaped by   a   shared   a - men,
sure - ly   your   pain   will   cease.

Cit - y   of   gold,   you   nev - er   grow
Guard - ian   of   dreams   each   new   day   re -
You   will   be   free   sim - ply   to

old   at   all. _____
deems   a - gain; _____
be   at   peace, _____

You laugh at the years,
en - cir - cling your fears with a wall.

So wea - ry and worn,
you shall be re - born,
but when?

to si - lence your guns
and let all your sons in - crease.

to Verse 3
to Verse 4
to Verse 5

5. Je - ru - sa - lem, we who have met you can nev - er let you die.

freely

Such love did be - get you, if I should for - get you, May my love be with-ered and dry! Je - ru - sa - lem, cry! One day you will dance and know why.

ritard.
slower
ritard.

Psalm 122
Ps 137:5-6

77/ Song of Songs

Words and Music by
Sr. Miriam Therese Winter

Freely

Here is the sign I give to you, Sign of the life I will

live with you, Sign of our cov-e-nant, that you re-call

Love linked to love link-ing one and all:

a tempo

Rhythmically

1. Come, come, my be-lov-ed,
2. Come, come, my be-lov-ed,
3. Come, come, my be-lov-ed,

Win-ter is o-ver, the rains are
Now the night beck-ons, fra-grant with
Come from the des-ert in-to de-

done. Come, wel-come to
flowers. Dream, dark is de-
light. Wake, wake in-to

laugh-ter. To love ev-er af-ter,
part-ing. The day that is start-ing
won-der, Fear not the thun-der

we run! Love is a gar-den. Here is the
is ours! Love is a foun-tain. O-pen its
or the night. Love is a fire. Fierce is its

Gen 9:11-13,16-17
Song 1:2; 2:10-16; 3:1-5; 4:9-15;
5:1-2; 7:10-13; 8:6-7

78/ Peace Like a River

Moderately

REFRAIN

Words and Music by
Sr. Miriam Therese Winter

Peace, like a riv-er, — flow-ing down from the Giv-er — of — peace. Live her! — Love her! — Come

1. 2. 3. to Verses / Final Ending

down! down! Love her! — Come down!

VERSES

1. In an-guish, in sor-row, in the
2. Her full breasts will nour-ish the
3. No peo-ple, — no — na-tion, comes

throes — of giv-ing birth, But may-be to-
child in the night. The dry bones will
forth in a day. The new world cre-

Repeat Refrain
poco rit.

mor-row, the joy of peace on earth. —
flour-ish, re-joic - ing at the sight of...
a-tion, de-mands we die this way for...

Is 65: 17-19; 66: 7-14

79/ Sun, Sand and Silence

Capo 2: Play Am
REFRAIN
With feeling

Words and Music by
Sr. Miriam Therese Winter

VERSES

1. Where the time flows on for-
2. Where the wa - ter springs from
3. Where the burn - ing sun seems

ev - er, A - cross the
dry - ness In a cool - ing,
end - less, Love shel - ters

face - less land.
sweet sur - prise, And the
you from harm, And

Long the climb to the ha - ven's rest, But
hap - py heart goes danc - ing on, While the
sends the night to com - fort you,

strong the help - ing hand.
hung' - ring spir - it cries.
Cra - dled in its arm.

Repeat Refrain

Hos 2:14,20
Mic 4:1-2

80/ Loving You

Words and Music by
Sr. Miriam Therese Winter

Ballad

1. Lov-ing you is wind on wa - ter, tur-bu-lence and__ storm. Lone - li - ness laced with laugh - ter, win - ter in - to__ warm. Lov-ing you is some - times sun - shine e - ven when it's rain - ing. Lov-ing you means I'll see you in a mil - lion fa - ces be - fore my jour - ney's through, Fol - low you to a mil - lion pla - ces for a trace of __ you. You're

2. Lov-ing you means no re - turn - ing, al - ways let - ting__ go, Start-ing o - ver, ev - er learn - ing, how well I__ know. The one I love is all a - round me in all the love I'm feel - ing. God a - bove,__ mov - ing on,__ part of me re - main - ing. let this love__ be your own love's re - veal - ing. I hear you reach - ing out to me in ev - 'ry an - guished cry, Temp-ting me to stop a - while and watch the sea - sons__ by.

108

test - ing me___ at ev - 'ry turn - ing where I
As I go, I'll go on liv - ing

taste your love a - new.
e - ven as I die.

There's noth-ing lost,
There's noth-ing lost,

it's just the cost of lov-ing you.___
it's just the cost of lov-ing you.___

1.

Noth- ing lost, it's the cost of lov-ing you.___
Noth- ing lost, it's the cost of

2.

lov - ing you, ___

noth-ing lost, just the cost of lov- ing ___

you.

Jn 14:23; 21:17

81/ How Lovely

Words and Music by
Sr. Miriam Therese Winter

Lyrically
REFRAIN*

How love-ly is your dwell-ing place.— I'm long-ing to look up-on your face— some day.

VERSES 1-3

1. I long for the Lord, my heart and flesh cry out for the Dis-tant One. Strong in the Lord, the pil-grim in jour-ney-ing, Turn-ing to flow-ing springs, dry ways, high-ways, my ways of life.
2. How wel-come the nest, a place to root and rest for the brood-ing bird. Wel-come the nest, pre-pared by the Lord for me, ha-ven, se-cu-ri-ty. Sing praise, al-ways, who dwell in him.
3. One day with the Lord is bet-ter than a thou-sand oth-er days. Trust in the Lord. Such bless-ings he holds in store, I'll wait be-side his door. Time spent in sin's tent can-not com-pare.

Repeat Refrain

VERSE 4

4. For he_____ is the sun. How won-der-ful and warm is the gift of day. See, ev-'ry one,_____ the fa-vor that love be-stows, ten-der-ness o-ver-flows.

How long _____ must my song, _____ must I long _____

Repeat Refrain

for him.

Psalm 84

82/ Be Reconciled!

With spirit

Key: F Capo 1ˢᵗ Play E

Words and music by
Sister Miriam Therese Winter

Refrain

Be ___ rec - on - ciled, one with an - oth - er. God is our Fa - ther. We are broth - ers and sis - ters in the Lord.

Verses

1. We long for one world, linked hand in hand, no one a stran - ger, no for - eign land.
2. When one is hurt - ing, all feel the pain. Share then the free - dom! Share then the gain!
3. Work for a fu - ture when war will cease, when we'll be one world liv - ing in peace.

Last time

Be ___ rec - on - ciled, one with an - oth - er. God is our Fa - ther. We are broth - ers and sis - ters in the Lord.

2 Co 5:17-20

83/ Living Water

Moderately

Words and music by
Sister Miriam Therese Winter

Liv - ing wa - ter in the des - ert,

Liv - ing wa - ter,

Liv - ing wa - ter, liv - ing wa - ter,

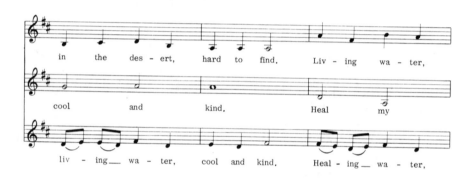

in the des - ert, hard to find. Liv - ing wa - ter,

cool and kind. Heal my

liv - ing __ wa - ter, cool and kind. Heal - ing __ wa - ter,

wash the des - ert, wash the des - ert of my mind.

heart and mend my mind.

heal - ing __ wa - ter, heal - ing wa - ter, heal __ my __ mind.

B

Still the thirst and chill the fe - ver,

Cool and cleanse, un -

Cool - ing wa - ter, cool - ing __ wa - ter,

source of strength, un - fail - ing spring. Cool and com - fort

fail - ing __ spring, cool and

cool - ing wa - ter, cool - ing __ spring; cool __ and com - fort,

the be - liev - er in the shad - ow of your __ wing.

com - fort - ing your wing.

cool and com - fort, cool and __ com - fort - ing your __ wing.

Is 41:17-18
Jn 7:37-39

*Sing the song simply, in unison,
or add ② for a two-part harmony,
even ③, if the group is able,*

84/ Happy the People

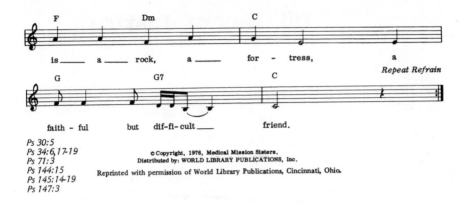

is __ a __ rock, a __ for - tress, a

Repeat Refrain

faith - ful but dif-fi- cult __ friend.

Ps 30:5
Ps 34:6,17-19
Ps 71:3
Ps 144:15
Ps 145:14-19
Ps 147:3

84a/ Mustard Seed

Words and music by
Sister Miriam Therese Winter

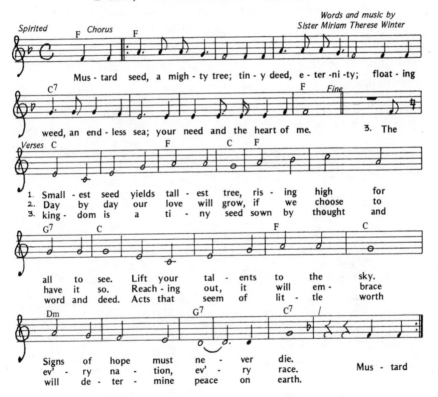

Spirited

Mus - tard seed, a migh - ty tree; tin - y deed, e - ter -ni -ty; float - ing

weed, an end - less sea; your need and the heart of me. 3. The

Verses

1. Small - est seed yields tall - est tree, ris - ing high for
2. Day by day our love will grow, if we choose to
3. king - dom is a ti - ny seed sown by thought and

all to see. Lift your tal - ents to the sky.
have it so. Reach - ing out, it will em - brace
word and deed. Acts that seem of lit - tle worth

Signs of hope must ne - ver die. Mus - tard
ev' - ry na - tion, ev' - ry race.
will de - ter - mine peace on earth.

Mt 13:31-32/Mk 4:30-32/Lk 13:18-19

85/ Day of Justice

Moderately slow

Capo 5: Play Am
REFRAIN

Words and Music by
Sr. Miriam Therese Winter

The spir - it of the liv - ing God has a - noint - ed me. Name a year of fa - vor. Set the peo - ple free. Pro - claim a day of jus - tice and _____ of lib - er - ty.

VERSES 1 and 2

1. Let good news be spo-ken to the poor.
2. Let all those in sad-ness be re - born.

Bind up hearts that are bro - ken. Help the
Clothe in gar - ments of glad - ness, com - fort,

weak to en - dure, and feed_____ the flocks. Feed_____
all those who mourn. Re - joice in the Lord. Re - joice

_____ the flocks!
in the Lord!

VERSE 3

Melody

3. In peace _____ and _____ bless - ing the poor _____ will

116

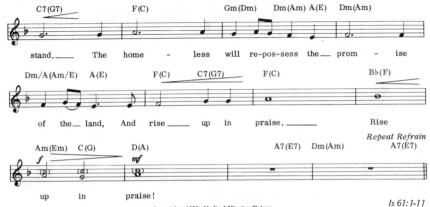

stand.___ The home - less will re-pos-sess the___ prom - ise
of the___ land, And rise_____ up in praise. _____ Rise
up in praise!

Repeat Refrain

Is 61:1-11
Lk 4:16-21

86/ Heavenly Father

Words and music by
Sister Miriam Therese Winter

Moderately

Heav-en-ly Fa - ther, hear your peo - ple whom your
Heav-en-ly Fa - ther, you once prom - ised to the

mer - cy has fed. We are plead - ing for your
world dai - ly bread. Take a bit from our

chil - dren who cry out for bread. So man - y
ta - ble, that all might be fed. ___ Gra-cious

hun - ger_____ for jus - tice and in their hun - ger have
Lord of_____ the har - vest, ___ give us plen - ty to

died. Heav - en - ly Fa - ther and Pro -
spare, and___ when some barns are

tec - tor, sure - ly you can pro - vide.
emp - ty, _____ help us to share.

Mt 6:9-11

87/ Rejoice Now!

Words and music
beginning line 4 by
Sister Miriam Therese Winter

Phil 4:4
Rev 19:6-7
The Church's ancient Easter hymn,
the Exsultet

88/ Peace-making Man

Hymn-style

Words and Music by
Sr. Miriam Therese Winter

1. He is the first-born from the dead. The
2. He is the im-age of God un-seen, Our
3. Ab-so-lute full-ness in him re-sides, Through

Church is his bod-y and he, its head.
vis-i-ble sign of what love can mean.
him re-con-cil-ing what sin di-vides.

In his own per-son he re-deemed our loss, Mak-ing
Through him and for him all the world was made, Find-ing
We shall con-tin-ue all that he be-gan, Mak-ing

peace through the blood of his cross.
peace in the price that he paid. 3. peace through this peace-mak-ing man.

rit.

* The upper harmony is to be added on verses 2 and 3 only.

Col 1:15-20

Words, melody, and harmony © Copyright, 1976, Medical Mission Sisters.
Distributed by: WORLD LIBRARY PUBLICATIONS, Inc.

Reprinted with permission of World Library Publications, Cincinnati, Ohio.

89/ This Is the Night

Moderately

Words and Music by
Sr. Miriam Therese Winter

1. This is the night when God de-
2. This is the night the pil-lar of

liv - ered those held cap - tive from their chains, led them
fire be - comes a bea - con of be - lief to___

dry - shod through the sea, out of slav - e - ry.
lead the peo - ple on, when hope is near - ly gone, un-

Free your peo - ple once a - gain. This is the
wav'r - ing joy con - sum - ing grief. This is the

night___ when Christ has ran - somed us and
night, ___ this is the night of nights most

paid the price of sin. The Pas - chal Lamb was
blessed since time be - gan, when death is our re -

slain, bring - ing peace through pain.
birth, with heav - en wed to earth.

We will fol - low where he's been. This is the
Praise God's rec - on - cil - ing plan. This is the

night, this is the night he rose tri -
night, this is the night of joy, of

um - phant from the grave, o - pened what was
sol - emn songs of praise, wash - ing guilt a -

sealed, for - gave and blessed and healed
way. The night shall be as day,

those _____ he _____ suf - fered death to save.
mourn - ing turned to danc - ing all our days.

O hap - py fault! O nec - es - sar - y sin! A

1.
new day rush - es in!

2.
new day rush - es in!

Ex 13:21; 14:29
I Tim 2:5-6
Rev 5:12
    The Great Preface of the
    Paschal Vigil

90/ All the Days

With spirit

Words and Music by
Sr. Miriam Therese Winter

REFRAIN

One thing in-deed I ask of the Lord and this do I seek; that I may dwell with the Lord all the days, all the days of my life! life!

seek; that I may dwell with the Lord all the days, all the days of my life! life!

molto rit.

1.2.3. *a tempo, slower* ♩ = 80 *to Verses* *Final Ending*

VERSES

1. Give to the Lord of your sub-stance And your barns will be filled with wheat and wine.
2. Lord, you search me and you know me. You know when I'm up and when I'm down.
3. Yah - weh's faith-ful-ness en-folds me. My heart and my flesh sing songs of joy.

accel. *Repeat Refrain*

Ps 27:4
Ps 84:2
Ps 139:1-2
Prov 3:9-10

91/ Come

Hymn-style

For higher key: use capo 2; Play D
(Sounds in key of E)

Words and Music by
Sr. Miriam Therese Winter

1. Come in - to the pres-ence of the Lord. You who are shat - tered,
2. All who are bro-ken shall be whole. Fly like a bird to its

be re - stored. ____ You shall be made new and
nest, my soul. ____ For once you have spent one

deep down in you his love will grow.
day in his tent, where will you go?

3. Come be - fore the Ho - ly One. O-pen like a flow - er to the

sun. ____ Come and be filled with

all he has willed for your own good.

4. Come in - to the pres-ence of the king. Come, my friends, come dance and

sing. ____ All you now in need the_ Lord God will feed with

his own life - giv - ing food.

Ps 23:1-2
Ps 34:17-18
Ps 84:3,10
Ps 100:2
Jn 6:51
Rev 21:5

92/ Lovesong

Gently
Capo 4: Play E

Words and Music by
Sr. Miriam Therese Winter

1. Love is pa - tient, love is kind, heal - ing the hurt heart, haunt-ing the mind. Love will go with you, till one day you'll find, Love must leave love be - hind.

2. Love is a rain - bow con- ceived in a storm. Love, in the cold war of life, is warm. Love will be wait - ing when eve - ning draws on, then one day, love may be gone.

3. Love is a moun-tain, cer - tain and strong, some-times a si - lence, some-times a song. Love will re-mem-ber the where and the when. Come, love, come a - gain.

4. Love will go ten - der-ly, ten - der-ly by, Teas - ing to laugh-ter, teach-ing to cry. Love will watch lov - ing-ly, let - ting you learn: some loves nev - er re - turn.

5. Love will flow on in-to

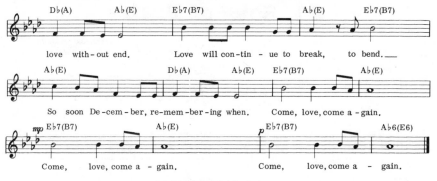

love with-out end. Love will con-tin - ue to break, to bend.

So soon De-cem - ber, re-mem - ber-ing when. Come, love, come a - gain.

Come, love, come a - gain. Come, love, come a - gain.

I Co 13:1-13

93/ What Do You Ask of Me?

Moderately

Words and Music by
Sr. Miriam Therese Winter

1. What do you ask of me?_____ What would you have me do?_____ I give my-self with - in_____ these gifts I of - fer you._____ This bread is food for life._____ This wine is spir - it of love for you.

2. What can I of-fer you._____ You've giv - en life to me._____ You're part of all I am._____ What would you have me be?_____ This bread is food for life._____ This wine is spir - it of love for me.

Ps 116:12-19

94/ Song of Praise

Driving beat

REFRAIN

Words and Music by
Sr. Miriam Therese Winter

Ho - ly, Ho - ly, Ho - ly, come, Lord! Ho - ly, Ho - ly, Ho - ly, come, Lord!

Ho - ly, Ho - ly, Ho - ly, come, Lord!

1. to Verses   Final Ending

VERSES

1. Lord, your glo - ry fills all cre - a - tion,
2. Come a - gain, O God of the liv - ing,

Ev - 'ry peo - ple and ev - 'ry na - tion.
God of good - ness, faith - ful, for - giv - ing.

All of life pro - claims your praise.
Touch with love our love - less ways.

Repeat Refrain

Is 6:3/Rev 4:8

Words, melody, and harmony © Copyright, 1971, Medical Mission Sisters.
Distributed by: WORLD LIBRARY PUBLICATIONS, Inc.

95/ Glory Be!

Words and Music by
Sr. Miriam Therese Winter

Glo - ry be to the Fa - ther, and to the Son, And to the Ho - ly Spir - it since the world was be - gun. As it was, and is now, and shall be with - out end. A - men, A - men, A - men! Glo - ry

95a/Amen!

Music by
Sister Miriam Therese Winter

A - men, A - men, men, A - men!

*The Doxology and the Amen
are basic scriptural acclamations.*

96/ Song of Peace

Moderately

Guitar: D, G, D, A7 progression throughout

Words and Music by
Sr. Miriam Therese Winter

CHOIR

Lamb of God, you take a - way our fail - ure to love.

Fill us with the warmth of your way.

O - pen us to ev - 'ry one who touch - es our life.

Help us reach each oth - er to - day.

Prince of Peace, come fill us with your peace with - out end.

Peace and love go with you, my friend.

ROUND STYLE
Congregation: Side 1

Peace to you, my friend, go in love.

Congregation: Side 2

Peace to you, my friend, go in

Peace to you, my friend, go in love.

love.

Choir

Peace to you, my ...

Lamb of God, you take a - way our fail - ure to ... *(etc.)*

(continue to end)

Is 9:6
Jn 1:29

96a/ Kingdom Song

Words and music by
Sister Miriam Therese Winter

Sing unaccompanied (Leader)

(All: Repeat line after Leader)

1. Sing, we sing of the King - dom.

Sing, we sing of the King - dom.

The King - dom of love. The King - dom of mer - cy.

Last time

Love will in - crease, the King - dom of peace.

Coda

Love will in - crease, the King - dom of peace.

Mt 6:33

2. Bring on, bring on the Kingdom . . .
The Kingdom of joy . . . the Kingdom of justice . . .

3. Work now, work for the Kingdom . . .
The Kingdom of hope . . . the Kingdom of promise . . .

4. Live, live, live for the Kingdom . . .
The Kingdom to come . . . the Kingdom among us . . .

5. Stand up, stand for the Kingdom . . .
The Kingdom within . . . now and forever . . .

*Sing Verse 4 and 5 each a half-tone higher.

97/ Fill My Emptiness

Simply

Words and Music by
Sr. Miriam Therese Winter

REFRAIN

Come, fill my emp-ti-ness.___ I love you more, not less,___ than ev-'ry-thing a-round that cap-tures my at-ten-tion.

VERSES

1. I love you more than the mys-ter-ies of the
2. I love you for the per-ma-nence of your
3. I love the bread that's bro-ken to be
4. I love the land in which___ my past is

1. sea-sons
2. be-ing.
3. eat-en
4. plant-ed,

That___ haunt me like a
In___ you there is no
From the bod-y that
Al-though I'm but a

1. fa-v'rite mem-o-ry.
2. ques-tion of good-bye.
3. bled up-on a tree.
4. pil-grim pass-ing by.

These gifts you've giv-en
And ev-'ry-thing that
I love the love that
I love the hand that

1. me are but the rea-sons
2. in-ter-rupts my see-ing,
3. lived to be un-beat-en,
4. holds my heart in bond-age,

I can
Is___
That's
And the

Repeat Refrain

1. love cre-a-tion ful-ly and be free.
2. but the love re-flec-ted in your eye.
3. of-fered in sur-ren-der now to me.
4. hun-ger on-ly he can sa-tis-fy.

Lk 1:53; 22:19
Rm 15:13
Heb 1:10-12; 13:14

98/ Seek Me

Words and Music by
Sr. Miriam Therese Winter

Brightly

REFRAIN 1

Seek Me with all your heart and I will let you find Me.

Seek Me! You are a part of all the love in Me.

VERSES

1. I am with you day by day though clouds of doubt con - ceal the way.
2. Seek the way My Word re - veals:__ Help-ing oth - ers helps and heals.
3. Seek for all that life can mean. The deep-est things re - main un - seen.

1. Faith will bil - low from a spark. Child, don't be a - fraid of the dark!
2. Take and make My love your own. Child, you'll nev - er be a - lone.__
3. Dare to dream and you will grow. Child, I'm all you need to know.__

REFRAIN 2

1-3. Search! It's My com-mand. Seek __ to un-der-stand.

Reach, I'm near at hand, fol-low-ing close be - hind.

[1.2.] Seek and you will find.

[3.] find...

fol-low-ing close be - hind... seek and find!

Ex 13:22
Is 55:6; 58:8
Jer 29:13-14

Words and melody © Copyright, 1976, Medical Mission Sisters.
Distributed by: WORLD LIBRARY PUBLICATIONS, Inc.

99/ Take This Bread

Words and music by
Sister Miriam Therese Winter

Moderately

1. Take this bread,____ take this wine,___
2. Take this heart.____ It is yours,__
3. Come a - mong ____ us in re - turn.____

____ as a prom - ise, as a sign.
____ ev' - ry strug - gle it en - dures,
____ In your pres - ence, may we learn

The life is yours, the love is mine.
   all the love it's made to hold,
that you and I and we are one,

Let our life and love com - bine.
all the warmth, all the cold.
and a new life has be - gun.

Mt 18:20
Mt 26:26-28/Mk 14:22-24
Jn 17:21-23

100/ Magnificat

Sister Miriam Therese Winter

Wyeth's *Repository of Sacred Music*

1. My soul gives glo - ry to the Lord. My
2. The Lord has done great things for me:
3. From age to age, to all who fear, such pro -
4. Love casts the might - y from their thrones, a -
5. The Lord is true to Is - ra - el,

heart pours out its praise. God
Ho - ly is this Name. All
mer - cy Love im - parts, dis -
motes the in - se - cure, leaves
lert to ev - 'ry need, re -

lif - ted up my low - li - ness in
peo - ple will de - clare me blessed, and
pens - ing jus - tice far and near, dis -
hun - gry spir - its sat - is - fied, the
mem - ber - ing past prom - is - es to

man - y mar - vel - ous ways.
bless - ings they shall claim.
miss - ing sel - fish hearts.
rich seem sud - den - ly poor.
A - bra - ham and his seed.

Lk 1:46-55

101/ Will You Be with Me?

Words and music by
Sister Miriam Therese Winter

Reflectively

1. Will you be with me _____ when I am
2. Will you be with me _____ when mem-'ry

old and gray, _____ when shad - ows length - en _____
starts to fade, _____ when life's sweet mu - sic _____

_____ at the close of day? _____ Will you be
has _____ all been played? _____ Will you con -

wait - ing _____ pa - tient - ly stand - ing by, _____
tin - ue _____ sing - ing a brand new song? _____

read - y to wel - come me know - ing why,
Will you re - mem - ber how I've loved you long?

all of my life - time, _____ I've want-ed to spend all of for -
All of my life - time, _____ I've want-ed to spend all of for -

ev - er with you with - out end.
ev - er with you with - out end.

Ps 27:4
Ps 71:9,17-23

102/ Thank You, God

Words and music by
Sister Miriam Therese Winter

Refrain *Moderately*

Thank you, God, for the gift of birth, for love made flesh to re - fresh the earth. For life and strength and length of days, we give you thanks and praise.

Verses

Lord, you pos - sessed me from the ve - ry start,
Your grace dis - co - vers me when my heart hides.
Lord, you cre - a - ted me for wan - ting you.

kept for your - self my un - sus - pec - ting heart.
If I should run from you, your love a - bides.
May you re - mem - ber me my whole life through.

Dt 30:19-20
Ps 71:6
Ps 139:1-18

103/ Listen!

Key: E CAPO: 2nd Play D

Words and music by
Sister Miriam Therese Winter

Refrain — Strong beat

Be o - pen! Hear the Good News in a rough, ir - reg - u - lar rhyme, the ca - dence of God's liv - ing Word in a tense and tur - bu - lent time.

Verses

1. Be still and lis - ten to the sounds of the world, to the mean - ing of its song. Lis - ten close - ly to a wa - ter - fall or a bird - call on the wing, to a child's con - ten - ted chat - ter - ing, each one's cher - ished thing.

2. Be still and lis - ten to the sounds of the world, to its loud and lone - ly song. Have you heard the one who's near to you, that shrill un - spo - ken cry? Do you lis - ten to those dear to you or do their lives go rush - ing by?

3. Be still and lis - ten to the sounds of the world. Do you ev - er sing a - long? Of - ten we are deaf and dumb. In - diff'rent - ly we stum - ble on, lis - t'ning for the fife and drum af - ter the pa - rade has gone.

Be tense and tur - bu - lent time, in a tense and tur - bu - lent time.

Ps 46:10
Heb 4:7,12-13

104/ Welcome to the Banquet

Words and music by
Sister Miriam Therese Winter

Brightly

Wel - come to the ban - quet of the Lord. We
Wel - come to the ban - quet of the Lord. We

ce - le - brate what you cre - ate. Our love has dared to
live a - gain your great a - men. We would be fed on

come pre - pared to risk all once we have heard the
li - ving bread, that we might have the strength to do the

clear call of your li - ving Word. Wel - come,
things we are com - mit - ted to. Wel - come,

Chris - tians. Wel - come, Chris - tians. Wel - come,
Chris - tians. Wel - come, Chris - tians. Wel - come,

Chris - tians to the ban - quet of the Lord.
Chris - tians to the ban - quet of the Lord.

Ps 23: 5
Jn 6: 51

105/ This Is My Body

Calypso rhythm

Words and music by
Sister Miriam Therese Winter

This is my Bo - dy which was bro - ken for you, take and
This is my Blood which was shed for you, take and
This is my love I sur - ren - der to you, take and
Here is my life and I give it to you for your

eat. This is my Bo - dy which was
drink. This is my Blood which was
share. This is my love I sur -
own. Here is my life and I

bro - ken for you, take and eat.
shed for you, take and drink.
ren - der to you, take and share.
give it to you for your own.

This is my Bo - dy which was bro - ken for you,
This is my Blood which was shed for you,
This is my love I sur - ren - der to you,
Here is my life and I give it to you.

as in the pro - mise I had spo - ken to you.
proof of a love that of - ten bled for you.
a hu - man love that's warm and ten - der to you.
Say but the word, I will come live it in you.

This is my Bo - dy which was bro - ken for the life of the
This is my Blood which was shed for the life of the
This is my love I sur - ren - der for the life of the
Here is my life, take and live it for the life of the

world.
world.
world.

world.

Mt 26:26-28/Mk 14:22-24/Lk 22:19-20/
I Co 11:23-25/Jn 6:51

106/ Wherever He Goes

Words and music by
Sister Miriam Therese Winter

Joyously

Bro - thers, sis - ters, hand in hand, lead us
Chris - tians, come join a - long. Let us
Saints in glo - ry, one and all, who kept
All who have run and won the race now

to the pro - mised land. You have
sing a brand new song, a song of
true to the Pro - phet's call, true to a
see God face to face, walk in the

passed through the Eas - tern Gate; re -
strife and vic - to - ry, a
vi - sion of things un - seen:
splen - dor of e - ter - nal light while

mem - ber us who watch and wait.
song we'll sing for e - ter - ni - ty:
teach us now what faith can mean:
we march on through dark of night.

Glo - ry, al - le - lu - ia, He died and rose. We

fol - low the Lamb wher - e - ver He goes.

Ez 10:19
I Co 9:24-25
2 Tim 4:7
Heb 11:1
Rev 7:9; 14:3-4

107/ Work While You Have the Light

Driving beat

Words and music by
Sister Miriam Therese Winter

Work while you have the light.
Work while you have the light.
Work while you have the light.

Soon the night will o - ver - take us all.
Soon our sight will blind us to the way.
Do your task though no - one un - der - stands,

Soon we'll fail to hear an - oth - er's call.
Soon the night will steal the light of day.
though your flocks now graze in oth - er lands.

Soon our pri - vate dream worlds must fall. But
Soon we'll lose the right to have our say.
Christ will bless the work of your hands.

Christ will lift our love from the dust.
Soon we'll not know quite how to pray, yet
When your day of dawn to dusk is done,

Last verse

Christ will come to save us if we trust.
Christ will keep the howl- ing hounds at bay.
Christ will be the

set - ting of your sun.

Jn 9: 4-5
1 Co 4:12

108/ We Are Gathered

Hymn-style

Words and music by
Sister Miriam Therese Winter

We are ga - thered here to - ge - ther,
We are ga - thered here to - ge - ther,

drawn by a grow - ing faith some say is gone.
ga - thered to ce - le - brate the Li - ving Bread.

We find strength in one an - o - ther,
We break bread for one an - o - ther,

and the con - fi - dence to car - ry on. The
hop - ing all who hun - ger will be fed. The

week has been hard, we seek a com - mu - ni - ty,
signs of the times, Lord, tell us to turn to you.

so we might of - fer a com - mon prayer. A
There is an ans - wer with - in your Word. To

war - ring world finds mean - ing in u - ni - ty.
love and be - lieve, Lord, this we would learn to do, and

Where Chris - tians ga - ther, God is there.
trust our prayers for peace are heard.

Mt 18:20
Lk 21:25-26
Jn 6:51

Copyright © Medical Mission Sisters, 1971.

141

109/ Offering Song

Moderately

Words and music by
Sister Miriam Therese Winter

Take this bread and wine as a
dreams have not come true, still we
bread that we would bring is the

to - ken of com - mit - ment. It re - pre - sents a
dare to go on dream - ing. The world we would re-
thing we have at - temp - ted, the thing we do and

love in which we've grown. With this
fash - ion has grown bold. Bless the
all we've left un - done. Let the

dish, with this cup, all our love we lift
stuff of our dreams. Bless our hope, for it
lives that we build be trans - formed and ful -

up to your own. 2. Our
seems tired and old. 3. The
filled in your Son.

Rm 12:2   Copyright © Medical Mission Sisters, 1971.
I Co 5:8; 10:16-17; 11:23-26

110/ Christ, Who Is My Joy

Freely

Words and music by
Sister Miriam Therese Winter

Verses

Hap - py are we who are called by God to
Hap - py are we who will fol - low God,
Hap - py are we who will wel - come God,
Hap - py are we who keep faith with God,

call forth Christ in the world:
fol - low Christ in the world:
wel - come Christ in the world:
faith - ful to Christ in the world:

Christ, Whom I have seen, Whom I have loved, in
Whom I have be - lieved, Who is my Joy.

Is 43:1
Mt 9:9; 25:35
Jn 20:18
2 Tim 4:7

110a/ Forgive Us, Lord

Words and music by
Sister Miriam Therese Winter

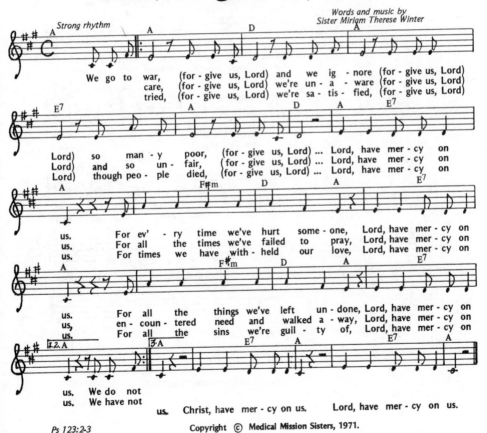

We go to war, (for - give us, Lord) and we ig - nore (for - give us, Lord)
care, (for - give us, Lord) we're un - a - ware (for - give us, Lord)
tried, (for - give us, Lord) we're sa - tis - fied, (for - give us, Lord)

Lord) so man - y poor, (for - give us, Lord) ... Lord, have mer - cy on
Lord) and so un - fair, (for - give us, Lord) ... Lord, have mer - cy on
Lord) though peo - ple died, (for - give us, Lord) ... Lord, have mer - cy on

us. For ev' - ry time we've hurt some - one, Lord, have mer - cy on
us. For all the times we've failed to pray, Lord, have mer - cy on
us. For times we have with - held our love, Lord, have mer - cy on

us. For all the things we've left un - done, Lord, have mer - cy on
us, en - coun - tered need and walked a - way, Lord, have mer - cy on
us. For all the sins we're guil - ty of, Lord, have mer - cy on

us. We do not
us. We have not
us. Christ, have mer - cy on us. Lord, have mer - cy on us.

Ps 123:2-3

111/ Keep Me

Reflectively

Words and music by
Sister Miriam Therese Winter

Keep me as the ap - ple of your eye. Hide
Keep me as the ap - ple of your eye. Hide
Keep me as the ap - ple of your eye. Hide

me in the sha - dow of your wings. Keep me
me in the sha - dow of your wings, from the
me in the sha - dow of your wings. In your

safe from e - vil things. I call on
dan - ger the day brings. My feet are
pre - sence my soul sings. You come by

you and my prayer is heard, your stead - fast
firm on love's good ground, though hate pur -
night. My heart is tried. I wake with

love, my stum - bling word ....
sues and fears sur - round.
morn - ing, sa - tis - fied. Keep

me as the ap - ple of your eye. Hide me in the

sha - dow of your wings, in the shel - ter of your wings, en -

fold me with your wings.

Psalm 17

112/ Come, Spirit

With spirit

Words and music by
Sister Miriam Therese Winter

Sing, my soul, a Spi - rit song,
Dance, my heart, at your re - birth,
When con - strained by thoughts or things,

call - ing all to sing a - long.
part - ner to the dance of earth.
hear the word the Spi - rit brings:

Fill the world with joy - ful sounds:
Thirst - ing spi - rit, drink your fill:
life is lar - ger than it seems,

God is here and grace a - bounds.
love goes dan - cing where it will.
hope is har - bin - ger of dreams.

Chorus

Come, Spi - rit, come and be a new re - al - i -ty.

Your touch is guar - an - tee of love a - live in me.

Rm 5:20
I Co 14:15
2 Co 1:22; 5:5

113/ Giving Thanks

With feeling

Words and music by
Sister Miriam Therese Winter

I'm gi - ving thanks for my me - mo - ries of you, for
I'm gi - ving thanks for ev' - ry - thing we've shared. Thanks for
I'm gi - ving thanks for the friend - ship that I feel, a
And so I pray love will claim you more and more, that the

all we have ac - com - plished in his name.
shar - ing both the cheers and the chains.
feel - ing so much deep - er than ap - pears.
love al - ready with - in you will grow and grow.

I want to tell you I'm so ver - y glad I came,
I want to tell you it was real - ly worth the pain,
I want to tell you how it was nur - tured here,
I want to tell you it is hard for me to go,

and I can tell you, it will ne - ver be the same.
and I can tell you, warm me - mo - ries re - main.
and I can tell you, it will lin - ger through the years.
and I can tell you, it's be - cause I love you so.

Coda

I'm gi -ving thanks for my me - mo - ries of you.

Phil 1:3-11

114/ You, Lord, Are My Firmament

Moderately

Words and music by
Sister Miriam Thérèse Winter

You, Lord, are my fir - ma - ment, roof for my
You, Lord, are a tower of strength. I shall not
You, Lord, are my guid - ing light, bea - con from

head, shel - ter from storm, nour - ish - ing
fear. I shall not fall. Lord, you are
birth, help - ing to see, light - ing the

bread, ten - der and warm. I will give
near, guard - ian of all.
earth, en - light - en - ing me.

(melody)
thanks. I will sing praise, with all of my
I will give thanks, sing praise, with all of my

(harmony)

heart, all of my days. days.
heart, all of my days. days.

Psalm 18

115/ Taste and See

Words and music by
Sister Miriam Thérèse Winter

Slowly, with solemnity

1. Taste and see   good - ness, you that hun - ger for the Lord.
2. To the crushed in spi - rit, O how bit - ter the wine.

Taste of love a - bun - dant - ly out - poured.
Taste this word of com - fort, you are mine. *(Refrain)*

Refrain

Taste of love and you will see at last. Turn to love and you will know.

Sa - vor love and you will grow in love. The Lord re - veals his pro - mise, the

Lord re - veals his pre - sence to all who call on him.

3. When I cry for mer - cy, bro - ken - heart - ed I plead, the
4. And my prayer is ans - wered, come and bless the Lord with me.

Lord is near to hear me in my need.
Let us praise his ways e - ter - nal - ly. *(Refrain)*

him,   to all who call on him.

Psalm 34

116/ Song of Trust

Prayerfully

Words and music by
Sister Miriam Therese Winter

O Lord, my heart is not proud, my
O Lord, my heart will not fear, though

spi - rit is bowed be - fore your ma - jes - ty.
dan - ger is near. Al - though the e - ne - my en--

Look at me, a child at rest. Your
cir - cles me, my heart will bless your

nur - turing breast re - stores my soul,
faith - ful - ness. I trust in you to

makes me whole a - gain.
see me through a - gain.

Psalm 131   Copyright ©   Medical Mission Sisters, 1982.

117/ Forgive Us All

Slowly, with feeling

Words and music by
Sister Miriam Therese Winter

It's ev' - ning, the sha - dows rise. A
It's morn - ing, the day a - wakes, as
For - e - ver the va - cant stares of
It's ev' - ning, the sha - dows fall on

lit - tle child cries for bread. While
help - less cries pierce the air. I'm
all of those long de - prived curse
all of those long op - pressed, while

I am fed, an - o - ther ba - by
un - a - ware an - o - ther spi - rit
those who thrived: an - o - ther age - des -
I am blessed. May God for - give us

dies ... an - o - ther ba - by dies.
breaks ... an - o - ther spi - rit breaks.
pairs ... an - o - ther age des - pairs.
all ... for - give us all.

Mt 6:12
Rm 4:7   Copyright © Medical Mission Sisters, 1982.

118/ Workers In The Vineyard

Verses With spirit

Words and music by
Sister Miriam Therese Winter

Wor - kers in the vine - yard of the Lord dif - fer from each
Wor - kers in the vine - yard of the world dif - fer from each
Wor - kers in the vine - yard of the heart dif - fer from each

o - ther. Some come ear - ly, some come late, some in a hur - ry and
o - ther. Drawn by the goal we're wor - king toward, lo - ving peace,
other. Some will strug - gle, some will play. Some will leave and

some would wait. It's up to God to e - val - u - ate those
lo - ving the Lord. Who would mea - sure love's re - ward when
some will stay, but love will have the fi - nal say with the

wor - king for the king - dom.
wor - king for the king - dom. Come, now, ev' - ry
com - ing of the king - dom.

wo - man, ev' - ry man. Work with a will. Work when you can. There's

much to be done since we be - gan to la - bor for the king - dom

Mt 20:1-16

119/ I Know, I Know

With feeling

Words and music by
Sister Miriam Therese Winter

Birth is sor - row, birth is pain.
A child was stan - ding on a time - less shore.
The day was bar - ren for the birds had flown.

Ev' - ry to - mor - row means a day's been slain.
In but a mo - ment, a child no more.
A Voice kept say - ing: "You're not a - lone.

The time runs swift - ly and the tide runs slow,
Some-times we cher - ish what might have been,
The coast is chan - ging and the cur - rent's deep.

for - e - ver shif - ting, how else to grow?
in - stead of lov - ing the love we're in.
Toss all your ter - rors in - to My keep.

I know, I know.
I know, I know.
I know, I know."

Gen 3:16
Jn 10:14; 14:18

120/ Have You Abandoned Me?

Words and music by
Sister Miriam Therese Winter

With intensity

The deeds of the brook are swal - lowed by the sea. The
The chil - dren of chance who did not have to die, con -
The poor con-sumed by hun - ger, the rich con-cerned with war, and

trees of the for - est de - ny e - qual - i - ty. My
demned by com - pla - cen - cy that has - n't learned to cry. My
mil - lions die who know not what they're dy - ing for. My

God, ——— have you a - ban - doned - me?
God, ——— have you a - ban - doned me?
God, ——— have you a - ban - doned me?

Life holds its se - crets we can't un - der - stand, and

God holds the world in the palm of His hand. In -

to His migh - ty po - wer this trou - bled world I

send, so that a stor - my be - gin - ning know a peace - ful end.

Ps 22:1
Is 49:16
Mt 27:46/Mk 15:34

121/ Watch and Pray

Words and music by
Sister Miriam Therese Winter

Moderately

The clouds will rain the Just One and the earth will yield its fruit. The wait-ing done, the a-wai-ted One will spring from Jes-se's root. Watch and pray. Christ comes a-gain. He'll claim us then, but we know not the hour or day.

God's hand will touch a vir-gin with the mys-ter-y of birth. Whose trust was tried will o-pen wide to wel-come God to earth. Watch and

His love will come like rain-drops up-on a thirs-ting field. He'll bring the spring and ev'-ry-thing will wa-ken and be healed. Watch and

The croo-ked will be straigh-tened, the moun-tains all laid low, and in that hour we'll feel His po-wer and know not where to go. Watch and

know not the hour or day.

Ps 72:6
Is 7:14/Mt 1:22-23
Is 11:1; 45:8
Is 40:3-5/Mt 3:3/Mk 1:2-3/Lk 3:4-6/Jn 1:23

122/ No Longer Afraid

Prayerfully

Words and music by *Sister Miriam Therese Winter*

When I look on a heart that is bro - ken, and I
When I think of the phra - ses un - spo - ken, what a
When I look on your love left as to - ken, on the

think of the part that I played. When the
diff' - rence a word would have made. When I'm
ban - quet your pro - mise has laid. When I

dam - age is done and I've star - ted to run, and I
star - ting to list all the chan - ces I've missed, all the
start to re - gret all the times I for - get, all the

run when I ought to have stayed, then I
friends that my fear has be - trayed, I re -
times that I ought to have prayed, then I

look on your woun - ded side, my God, and my
call how your friends all fled, my God, and my
run to your flesh and blood, my God, and my

heart is no lon - ger a - fraid. My
heart is no lon - ger a - fraid. My
heart is no lon - ger a - fraid. My

heart is no lon - ger a - fraid.
heart is no lon - ger a - fraid.
heart is no lon - ger a - fraid.

Mt 26:56/Mk 14:50
Mt 26:26-28/Mk 14:22-24/Lk 22:19-20
Jn 19:34,37

123/ Praise To the Lord

Spirited

Words and music by
Sister Miriam Therese Winter

Refrain D   F#m   Bm

When ev' - ry help is gone, be strong and car - ry on, for the

Em   G   A7   D   *Verses*

Lord   is   on   our   side.

1. We
2. From
3.

A

went with the Lord in - to the val - ley of death. He
day - light to dark in - to the dread of the night, the
All who are frigh - tened and a - fraid of your fear,

felled the foe with his fire - y breath. Our
e - ne - my ad - vanced un - til we trem - bled with fright. The
things aren't as bad as they are made to ap - pear.

peb - bles of prayer o - ver - came Go - li - ath.
Lord God turned them with his ter - ri - ble might.
Peace! for the Lord our Sa - vior is here.

A9   A   D

The Lord has con - quered! Praise to the Lord!
The Lord has con - quered! Praise to the Lord!
The Lord has con - quered! Praise to the Lord!

I Sam 17:49-50
Ps 71:4
Ps 118:5-7
Acts 2:25-28
Rev 17:14

124/ One Love Never Dies

Play in Key of G - minor, or
Capo 3, play in Key of E - minor

Words and music by
Sister Miriam Therese Winter

1. Why must some-thing so beau-ti-ful die? Day in-to night, steal-ing the
2. Why must some-one so beau-ti-ful die? Gone the de-light, the feel and the

light, and I'm a-lone a-gain, on my own a-gain.
sight, and I'm a-lone a-gain, on my own a - - gain.

Some loves live for-e-ver. One love ne-ver dies.

Like a tent, it's mo-ment spent, rolled up and car-ried on.

Like a thread in the wea-ver's shed, rolled up, cut off, and gone.

3. Why must some-thing so beau-ti-ful die? Sum-mer to Fall, leav-ing me
4. Why must some-one so beau-ti-ful die? No more to give, how shall I

all a-lone a-gain, on my own a-gain.
live a-lone a-gain, on my own a - - gain.

Some loves live for-e-ver. One love ne-ver dies.

Like the grass, we too will pass and no-thing will re-main.

Pain and fears and un-shed tears will ne-ver hurt a-gain.

5. Why must some-thing so beau-ti-ful die? Fade in - to time, and sud-den-ly
   I'm a-lone a - gain, on my own a - gain.
6. Why must some-one so beau-ti-ful die? Love slip-ping by, and sud-den-ly
   I'm de-prived a - gain. God make me a - live a - gain.

Is 38:10-13
Is 40:6-8/I Pet 1:23-25
Jn 11:25

125/ Therefore, Choose Life

Moderately

Words and music by
Sister Miriam Therese Winter

Refrain
There-fore, choose life. Love a-lone re-news life. Live pre-pared to lose life.

Verses
Christ came that we might have life and have it in a-bun-dance. He
Christ came that we might have life ac-cor-ding to His pro - mise, ac -

came to show us how to grow and how to give.
cor-ding to His jus - tice and ac-cor - ding to His word.

Dy - ing, He de-stroyed our death and rose to give life mean - ing. His
Ris - ing, He re-stored our hope in life and re-sur-rec - tion. The

gift to us: He gave to us His life that we might live.
good news of His life is still the best news we have heard.

Dt 30:19
Ps 103:5
Ps 119:107,154,156
Mt 10:39; 16:25/Mk 8:35/Lk 17:33
Jn 10:10,15; 11:25; 15:13
I Co 15:20-21,54-55
2 Co 4:16

126/ Joseph

Key of E♭, or
Capo 3, play in Key of C

Words and music by
Sister Miriam Therese Winter

Lyrical folk - style

Jo - seph, pro - tec - tor of the Lord, we sel - dom hear your
Jo - seph, pro - tec - tor of the Word, we do as you have
Jo - seph, pro - tec - tor of the Lord, we keep your mem' - ry

name. The gift of fi - del - i - ty was your re - ward, we
done, li - ving the dai - ly, si - lent - ly, in the
still, as one with the cour - age and faith to make ad -

la - bor for the same. You stayed in the sha - dow
shel - ter of your son. Con - tent with our call, we
just - ments to God's will. We would have com - pas - sion

far from praise, and when your life was done, the
car - ry on in faith, as you did then, while
and be wise in the wis - dom from a - bove, that

on - ly a - chieve - ment re - cor - ded for your days was the
know - ing we too will be long, long gone when
one day, like you, we might real - ly re - a - lize that we

guard - ing of God's own Son.
Eas - ter comes a - gain.
too have lived with

Love.

Mt 1:24-25
Lk 2:48,51

127/ Mary-Song

Words and music by
Sister Miriam Therese Winter

Lightly

1. Reed of God, emp - ty cup, Eas - tern Gate lif - ted up,
2. Si - lent spring, Wis - dom-child, fruit - ful field un - de - filed.

ev' - ning song, Mor - ning Star: La - dy, you are. *(Verse 2)*
May your care ne - ver cease, La - dy of Peace.

Cause of our Joy, Cause of our Joy! Cause of our Joy, Cause of our Joy!

Guide us on our pil - grim way. Keep us close both night and day.

Reed of God, emp - ty cup, Eas - tern Gate lif - ted up,
Cause of our Joy, Cause of our Joy!

ev' - ning song, Mor - ning Star: La - dy you are.
Cause of our Joy, Cause of our Joy!

Si - lent spring, Wis - dom - child, fruit - ful field un - de - filed.
Guide us on on our pil - grim way

May your care ne - ver cease, La - dy of Peace.
Keep us close both night and day.

(All) Guide us on our pil - grim way. Keep us close both night and day.

Lk 1:48

128/ Let Your Light Shine

Hymn - style

Verses

Words and music by
Sister Miriam Therese Winter

Yah - weh re - mem - bered us and called us by name. From
car - ry the good news of new life to all lands, through
We as com - mu - ni - ty re - spond to our call. The

ma - ny cul - tures, ma - ny na - tions, we came. God
joy - ful cour - age and the work of our hands, that
Word that shapes us has a mean - ing for all. Re -

binds us to - ge - ther with a com - mon con - cern, guides our
light pierce the dark - ness, that the bro - ken be healed, that the
born in the Spi - rit, we choose laugh - ter and tears, gi - ving

go - ing and guards our re - turn.
love of the Lord be re - vealed.
praise all the days of our years.

So let

Refrain

(melody)

your light shine in us and in all we do, and may all who
your light shine in all, in all we do, and may all who

So let your light shine in all, in all we do, and may all who

see our deeds give glo - ry, Lord, to you. 2. We you.

Ps 50:5
Ps 106:47
Ps 121:8
Is 43:1
Is 52:7/Rm 10:15
Mt 5:14-16

129/ Hymn To Hope

Play in C-minor
or
Key of A-minor, Capo 3
Moderately

Words and music by
Sister Miriam Therese Winter

Peo - ple who love the li - ving Word, peo - ple di - verse - ly gif - ted,
One bo - dy bound by com - mon cause, shar - ing in joy and sor - row,
We take our stand be - side the poor, join in their li - ber - a - tion,
Our hope is in the Word- made-flesh, who shared our own con - di - tion,
Spi - rit of jus - tice, be our guide, nur - ture the hope we cher - ish,

drawn to a gos - pel dim - ly heard, we come with hopes up - lif - ted,
led by the Spi - rit now to pause on the thres - hold of to - mor - row:
strug - gle to - geth - er to en - sure a suff - 'ring world's sal - va - tion,
send - ing his Spi - rit to re - fresh those faith - ful to his mis - sion.
Now is our mo - ment to de - cide if love will live or per - ish.

ga - thered in u - ni - ty and in praise, one in the prayer our voi - ces raise:
come, let us cel - e - brate and re - call God- gi - ven grace that shaped us all:
in sol - i - dar - i - ty with their pain, har -ness-ing hun - ger, brea - king chains:
Fol - low - ing Je - sus, we live and die, lift up in him the whole world's cry:
Faith in the fu - ture is on the line. Let our com - mit - ment be a sign:

Refrain

Come, Spi - rit of love, Spi - rit of life, broad - en our vi - sion.

Come, come and in - crease a spi - rit of hope, Spi - rit of peace.

Lk 4:18
I Co 12:4-13
Phil 1:27-29; 2:1-4

Mass of a Pilgrim People

Music by
Sister MIRIAM THERESE WINTER

130/Lord, Have Mercy

131/Glory to God

Music by
Sister MIRIAM THERESE WINTER

world, have mer - cy on us.
You, who take a - way the sins of the
world, re - ceive our prayer.
You, who sit at the right hand of the
Fa - ther, have mer - cy on
us. _____ For you a - lone are
ho - ly. _____ You a - lone are Lord.
You a - lone, O Je - sus Christ, are
most high, _____
with the Ho - ly Spir - it, _____ in the glo - ry of God the
Fa - ther. _____
men. _____

Lk 2:14

132/Holy! Holy! Holy!

Music by
Sister MIRIAM THERESE WINTER

Rhythmically

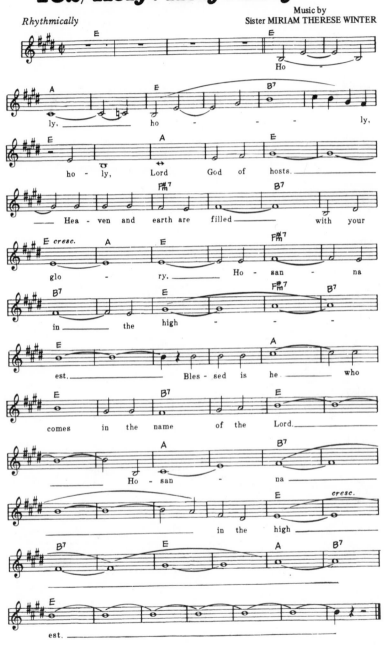

Ho - ly. ho - - - ly, ho - ly, Lord God of hosts. Hea - ven and earth are filled with your glo - ry. Ho - san - na in the high - - - est. Bles - sed is he who comes in the name of the Lord. Ho - san - na in the high - est.

Is 6:3/Rev 4:8
Lk 19:38

133/Our Father

Music by
Sister MIRIAM THERESE WINTER

Mt 6:9-13/Lk 11:2-4

134/ Lamb of God

Music by
Sister MIRIAM THERESE WINTER

Slowly

Lamb of God, You take a - way the sins of the world, have mer - cy on us. Lamb of God, You take a - way the sins of the world, have mer - cy on us. Lamb of God, You take a - way the sins of the world, grant us peace.

Jn 1:29

RSVP: Let Us Pray

Words and Music by
Sister MIRIAM THERESE WINTER

135/Lord, Have Mercy On Your People

Down in the ghet-to the blood flows free. There is re-bel-lion in the u-ni-ver-si-ty. Who is the guil-ty, is it they or is it we? Lord, have mer-cy on your peo-ple. Lord, have mer-cy. Christ, have mer-cy. Lord, have mer-cy on your peo-ple. We're un-con-cerned with the pau-per's lot. The rich get rich-er and the poor do not; yet still our hearts are co-vet-ing what we have-n't got. Lord, have mer-cy on your peo-ple. Lord, have mer-cy Christ, have mer-cy. Lord, have mer-cy on your peo-ple.

The world is scarred with the wounds of war, Torn by a vi-o-lence we can-not ig-nore. But still we're con-tri-bu-ting to what we de-plore. Lord, have mer-cy on your peo-ple. Lord, have mer - cy. Christ, have mer - cy. Lord, have mer-cy on your peo - ple.

Ps 123:3

136/Who Am I To Sing of Glory?

Words and Music by
Sister MIRIAM THERESE WINTER

Ps 8:4-5   Lk 2:13-18; 4:18   Rm 11:33-36
Mk 10:45   Jn 1:14

137/Lord, I Really Do Believe

Words and Music by
Sister MIRIAM THERESE WINTER

Refrain: Rhythmically — with feeling

Lord, I real-ly do be-lieve, help me if I'm doubt-ing. In the si-lence of your might-y Word I hear my own will shout-ing.

Last time to Coda

Verses:

Look, the world that I per-ceive!___ Tell me, can I still be-lieve?___
Look, is this Chris-tian con-cern to have to let our cit-ies burn to

What can my small love a-chieve when such a num-ber ache and
make the right-eous stop and turn?___ Great the les-sons that we

grieve _____ a - lone?
learn _____ a - lone.

Melody *Da Capo*

And He be - came Flesh.
And He be - came Flesh.

Coda

Lord, I real-ly do be-lieve, help me if I'm doubt-ing.___

rall.

Mk 9:24
Jn 1:14

138/Holy! Holy! Holy!

Words and Music by
Sister MIRIAM THERESE WINTER

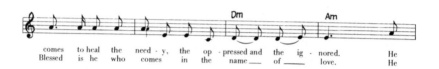

Ho - ly! Ho - ly! Ho - ly! to Christ the ___ Lord; who
Ho - ly! Ho - ly! Ho - ly! to God a - bove. ___

comes to heal the need - y, the op - pressed and the ig - nored. He
Blessed is he who comes in the name ___ of ___ love. He

comes ___ bring - ing peace ___ and his peace is by the sword.
comes ful - fill - ing prom - i - ses he told ___ us ___ of.

Let us sing: Ho - san - na in the high - est.
Let us sing: Ho - san - na in the high - est.

Coda

Let us sing: Ho - san - na in the high - est. ___

Is 6:3/Rev 4:8
Mt 4:24; 10:34
Lk 19:38

139/Yes!

Words and Music by
Sister MIRIAM THERESE WINTER

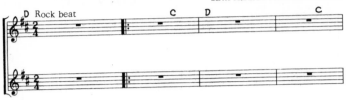

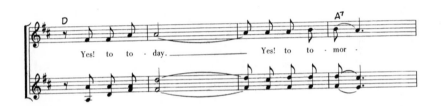

Yes! to cel - e - bra - tion.____ Yes! to sor - row.
(Unison first time)

Yes! to to - day.____ Yes! to to - mor -

row. Yes! to you, Lord, ____ and all you send. ____

Yes! Lord, Yes! A - men, a - men!

2 Co 1:19-20

140/God, Our Father

Words and Music by
Sister MIRIAM THERESE WINTER

1. God, our Fa-ther, who came to earth in Je-sus Christ, your Son. Bless-ed be your ho-ly name, And let your will be done.

2. Give us the bread we hun-ger for. We'll eat it on the run. May your king-dom come to us, And let your will be done.

3. Heal the ha-treds that we hold. Make your peo-ple one. For-give us for the times we fail, and

4. Turn us from our e-vil ways. Turn us to your Son. May we bless you all our days, and

Mt 6: 9-13/Lk 11:2-4

let your will be done.
let your will be done, and
let your will be done.

141/Peace To You, World

Words and Music by
Sister MIRIAM THERESE WINTER

Rock beat

Melody

Peace to you, world, deep in dis-il-lu-sion.

Peace to those ex-ploi-ted, with re-bel-lion in their heart.

Peace to peo-ple pulled to rev-o-lu-tion and con-fu-sion.

Peace to those who build and all of you _____ who tear a-part.

Peace, _____ and I pray _____ that his love _____

rall. 2nd time

_____ wipe your wounds _____ a-way.

way. _____

Jn 20: 21

Songs of Promise

Words and Music by
Sister MIRIAM THERESE WINTER

142/Lord, Have Mercy

mer - cy, for we tend to wan - der far a - way from you. Lord, have mer - cy, for the things we would not, these we seem to do. Lord,___ Lord,___ Lord,___ have mer cy.___ have___ mer cy.

Rm 7:15-20
Heb 4:16

143/Glory to God

Words and Music by
Sister MIRIAM THERESE WINTER

Brightly

1. Glo - ry to God in the high - est.___ Peace to
2. Heav - en - ly King, Lord and Sav - ior, you take a -

all up - on the earth. Praise to the Fa - ther,
way our sins and then, Through your___ dy - ing and

Son and Spir - it: we be - long to God by birth.
ris - ing, we are re - con - ciled to God a - gain.

Praise to Je - sus Christ our
Seat - ed now at God's right

Lord, who comes as God's own heal - ing Word. God's first
hand.___ One who one - time walked our land. Lord, your

prom - ise was a Son. Praise to the ho - ly migh - ty
King - dom is not far. Our heav - en___ is wher - e - ver you

1. D
One.

2. D
are.___

143a/ Alleluia

Words and Music by
Sister MIRIAM THERESE WINTER

Freely
D Intro.   D   Bm   Bm7

Al - le - lu - ia!   Al - le -

Al - le - lu - ia!

D   F#m Last time   D

lu - ia!   Al - le - lu - ia!

Al - le - lu - ia!

Verse:
D   D7   G

Your___ Word is a prom - ise in - deed. Your___

D   G A D   Coda D

Word is an an - swer to my need.   ia!

Ps 119:49-50

144/Yes, I Believe

Words and Music by
Sister MIRIAM THERESE WINTER

Rock beat

1. Yes, I be-
lieve _____ that my God lives.
who called him son.
I know the splen - dor _____ his pres - ence

woman _____ who called him son.
Light in the dark - ness hard - ly a
gives _____ to ev - 'ry-thing a -round me. That he be-

fail - ure _____ no one de - nies.
We too must lose _____ to win the
one _____ to re - cog-nize him. But from the
prize _____ of e - ter - nal glo - ry. And all the

came a man, _____ one born to die, this I be - lieve,
ash - es _____ of a blood - y cross, he leaped in tri - umph,
an - guish _____ I now per - ceive, he does al - low.

Last time

but I don't know why.
oh hap - py loss.

2. There was a
3. He was a

This I be - lieve!   This I be - lieve, I be-lieve, I be-

lieve, I be-lieve, I be - lieve,   I be - lieve.

Lk 17:33
Jn 1:9-11
Rm 14:7-9

145/ Holy! Holy!

Words and Music by
Sister MIRIAM THERESE WINTER

Mt 21:9
Lk 21:27
1 Co 11:26
2 Co 1:20-22

146/Acclamation

Words and Music by
Sister MIRIAM THERESE WINTER

I Co 11:26

146a/Amen

Music by
Sister MIRIAM THERESE WINTER

2 Thess 1:5,11

147/The Lord's Prayer

Music by
Sister MIRIAM THERESE WINTER

Mt 6:9-13/Lk 11:2-4

148/Peace Be With You

Words and Music by Sister MIRIAM THERESE WINTER

Jn 20:21 / 2 Co 6:16; 13:11 / Rev 7:14

149/ Holy! Holy! Holy!

Music by
Sister Miriam Therese Winter

With solemnity

(melody)
Ho - ly! Ho - ly! Ho - ly! Lord of pow-er and ma - jes - ty.

(harmony: optional)

Hea - ven and earth are filled with your glo - ry, O God most high.

Ho - ly! Ho - ly! Ho - ly! Lord of pow-er and ma - jes - ty.

Bles - sed is He who comes in the name of the Lord.

Ho - ly! Ho - ly! Ho - ly! Lord of pow-er and ma - jes - ty.

Hea - ven and earth are filled with your glo - ry, O God most high.

Is 6:3/Rev 4:8
Mt 21:9/Mk 11:9/Lk 19:38

150/Give Us Today

Words and music by
Sister Miriam Therese Winter

Moderately

God, our Fa-ther who lives in us. Blessed be your won-der-ful name.

Let your king-dom come to earth, the king-dom of your Son who came.

1. Give us to-day our ne-ces-sa-ry bread, by
2. For-give us, Lord, and all who do us wrong, and

which our bo-dies and souls are fed. Give us life. Give
in temp-ta-tion make us strong. Pro-tect our lives from

us your Son. And may your will in us be done.
e-vil, Lord, and let your love be

our re-ward, and let your love be our re-ward.

Mt 6:9-13/Lk 11:2-4

INDEX OF TITLES

* Publisher/Publication

INDEX OF THEMES